'*Kranti Nation* . . . is a ric
technologies are disrupting
mobility and healthcare to b
Prof. Klaus Schwab, Executi World Economic Forum

'We may interpret kranti as revolution, as Pranjal Sharma does, but in Sanskrit, the word also means course/trajectory, including that of the sun. Is India on that technology trajectory? Pranjal's delightful chronicling of fifty cases, many unknown and in unexpected segments, conveys a sense of optimism'
Bibek Debroy, Chairman, Economic Advisory Council of Prime Minister

'*Kranti Nation: India and the Fourth Industrial Revolution* ... will build the much-needed awareness of how entire sectors are transforming in response to the wave of disruptive technologies collectively known as the Fourth Industrial Revolution'
Chandrajit Banerjee, Director General, The Confederation of Indian Industry

'Pranjal Sharma brings the power of technical change and innovation to life in a thoroughly engaging way, through dozens of original cases of companies in India ... and shows that there are fortunes to be made in this Kranti Nation'
Dr Naushad Forbes, Co-chairman – Forbes Marshall, and ex-President – CII

'India is changing, and *Kranti Nation* provides ample number of examples of it'
Anirudh Damani, Blogger, showmedamani.com

'Mr Sharma states upfront that this book is a chronicle of how Indian businesses have adapted to the universally accepted irreversibility of 4IR . . . [it is] a rich tapestry of anecdotes'
Business Standard

'*Kranti Nation* is a proud presentation of the speed with which Indian industry leaders have brought . . . technologies into their mainstream activities . . . Pranjal Sharma's concise presentation of several companies and their progress in the use of Artificial Intelligence and Robotics is an eye-opener is more ways than one'
Free Press Journal

'The revolution is happening now, and *Kranti Nation* chronicles the how'
Global Calcuttan

'The author points out that it is not the big IT companies which are the prominent players of this big transformation . . . Rather, it is the local firms which are adopting new technologies to align with the new world order dictated by AI, and other things'
Print

'It may be a new concept for many of us, but it's time we updated ourselves about its endless possibilities, because sooner, rather than later, the Fourth Industrial Revolution is going to change the way we do business'
Print Week

'In *Kranti Nation* . . . Pranjal Sharma . . . gives us 50 examples of the burgeoning Fourth Industrial Revolution from 10 different sectors . . . Sharma alerts us to the fact that the Fourth Industrial Revolution has begun to transform Indian industry'
Times of India

KRANTI NATION

Pranjal Sharma is an economic analyst, advisor and columnist who focuses on technology, globalization and media. He has edited and written books and papers on entrepreneurship, business transformation and economic policy. He has held leadership positions in print and television media for over twenty-five years with organizations like the Times of India Group, India Today Group, CNBC Network 18 and Bloomberg UTV.

Pranjal has served on the Global Agenda Council of the World Economic Forum for eight years and is now a member of its Expert Network. He also guides projects on business intelligence and economic trend forecasting for Indian and global organizations.

www.pranjalsharma.com

KRANTI NATION

India and the Fourth Industrial Revolution

Pranjal Sharma

PAN

First published in India 2017 by Macmillan
First published in paperback 2018 by Pan
an imprint of Pan Macmillan Publishing India Private Limited
707, Kailash Building
26, K. G. Marg, New Delhi – 110 001
www.panmacmillan.co.in

Pan Macmillan, 20 New Wharf Road, London N1 9RR
Basingstoke and Oxford
Associated companies throughout the world
www.panmacmillan.com

ISBN 978-93-86215-61-1

1 3 5 7 9 8 6 4 2

Typeset by Manmohan Kumar
Printed and bound in India by Gopsons Papers Ltd.

'Do not be afraid of a small beginning,
great things come afterwards'

SWAMI VIVEKANANDA

CONTENTS

FOREWORD

I first spoke to Pranjal Sharma about the Fourth Industrial Revolution in Delhi in 2015. I am delighted to see that our conversation has developed into this rich account on how the Fourth Industrial Revolution is unfolding and impacting Indian industries, businesses and citizens.

Today we stand on the brink of a technological revolution that is changing how we work, live, learn, love, relate to one another and even what it means to be human. The pace, scale and complexity of the revolution will not just have profound impact on every country across the world, but will challenge existing business models, institutions and assumptions about the way the world works. Accordingly, it is critical that all stakeholders take the time to reflect on the future that is unfolding – not just to understand and adapt to the Fourth Industrial Revolution, but also to take every opportunity to make sure that it is a future that benefits us all.

Kranti Nation: India and the Fourth Industrial Revolution offers a glimpse into how Indian companies and innovators are already using powerful emerging technologies to transform organizations and entire sectors across India. It is a rich and comprehensive account of how technologies are disrupting and reshaping industries from mobility and healthcare to banking, agriculture and manufacturing. Pranjal presents a wealth of examples, which reveal a society already transforming as new technologies are developed, employed and reimagined to multiple ends. From Renault India's use of industrial robots to lower weight, emissions and price of their cars to Educomp's technology-based learning tools or the Kirloskar Brothers Ltd.'s use of 3D printing – this book abounds in examples of how technologies can and are already transforming the way that Indian organizations are creating value, both as national leaders and as examples for the world.

This book shows the three ways that India is at the forefront of the Fourth Industrial Revolution. First, Indian businesses and industry are demonstrating how global technologies can be tailored for local needs and customs, benefitting Indian citizens and consumers through greater economic opportunities and higher quality goods and services. Second, Indian innovators are creating new products and services with global applicability and scalability. And third, Indian companies and technology leaders are working to ensure that innovative technological solutions generate more than this economic upside – that they are developed in ways to increase inclusion and help address local challenges.

Perhaps *Kranti Nation's* most important contribution is that it can serve as a starting point for conversations about how to make India's experience and leadership of the Fourth Industrial Revolution both human-led and human-centred. It is only if new technologies are designed and implemented in a sustainable, inclusive and values-driven way that they will fully contribute to the long-term prosperity of India's economy and society. To achieve that, it is important that stakeholders across all groups of society are involved in debating the many ways that technology is changing the lives and hopes of India's 1.3 billion citizens, that positive narratives can materialize to the benefit of the many, not the few.

The book provides an optimistic account of the possibilities and opportunities the Fourth Industrial Revolution represents. However, as we enter a new era for humankind we must not shy away from addressing the potential negative impacts and challenges. These are many unless we act boldly where strong leadership is required, and cautiously where risks abound. The challenge is knowing the difference and responding accordingly.

For example, like in all countries today, India's business community and government must decide how and when to take advantage of the opportunities represented by automation. Yet youth unemployment across the country is worryingly high, particularly in the urban areas, and the economy needs to generate entirely new opportunities for the 12–13 million new university graduates who come into the workforce every year. If the Fourth Industrial Revolution is to bring optimism and prosperity to the young and future generations, managing the challenge of skilling young people and workers in high-risk jobs for a new world is a pivotal task for all political and business leaders.

It will take focus and effort to ensure that the new technology age translates into broad-based gains for India's population. One concern is that the most important infrastructure for the Fourth Industrial Revolution – the Internet – is still only available for less than half of India's population. Meanwhile, rising economic inequality undermines the sustainability of economic growth, undermines efforts to end extreme poverty and cascades into inequalities in health, education – all areas which affect a country's ability to gain from the Fourth Industrial Revolution.

I believe this book will serve to inspire readers to think, discuss and invest in a society where new technologies are thoughtfully deployed to the benefit of current and future generations in India. Moreover, I'm sure that the stories and examples in this book will inspire leaders and entrepreneurs in other emerging economies to find and highlight their own opportunities to harness the Fourth Industrial Revolution, thereby increasing the chance for even greater numbers of people to experience a prosperous and inclusive future.

Prof. Klaus Schwab
Executive Chairman and Founder
World Economic Forum

INTRODUCTION

Indian industry has always been buffeted by winds of transformation and revolution, and over the years, it has embraced change to emerge resilient and stronger. Today, a new kind of change driven by knowledge, creativity and connectivity is transforming the world. *Kranti Nation: India and the Fourth Industrial Revolution* is the kind of book that will spark India's closer engagement with these new trends. The book captures the beginnings of a new model of industry that Indian companies are just beginning to adopt and as such, it will build the much-needed awareness of how entire sectors are transforming in response to the wave of disruptive technologies collectively known as the Fourth Industrial Revolution.

The term Fourth Industrial Revolution is an umbrella concept that includes several emerging technologies such as artificial intelligence, robotics, big data, cloud, 3D printing or additive manufacturing, and the Internet of Things (IoT), among others. Although many of these technologies have been underway for several decades, they are now consolidating and converging. Machines may be seamlessly connected to each other in a factory unit, communicate with each other for identifying problems before they arise and devise solutions without human interface. Consumers too are more connected to the Internet through different devices and use a wide range of applications for different purposes, including through wearables, smart appliances, and e-commerce. Governments are deploying big data to understand trends and calibrate their policy responses. Connected infrastructure, smart urbanization, the spread of social media, mobile Internet, and other new technologies are creating new disruptions and business models at an ever-accelerating pace. In fact, the key characteristic of the Fourth Industrial Revolution appears to be the very rapid speed at which developments are sweeping across the economic landscape.

The combination of different technologies is changing our lives in many ways. First, the distance between producers and consumers is no longer relevant to creating markets. Customized products are possible, meeting the tastes of niche consumers without having to shift production lines. With producers and consumers on the same page, the entire meaning of what constitutes a market is changing.

Second, the lines between manufacturing and services have blurred. While services such as trading, finance, marketing and others were always closely connected to manufacturing, new services such as software, telecommunications, design and innovation, and content are now increasingly embedded in products and are an integral part of them. Industry 4.0 derives greatly from a strong backbone of services of different kinds, such as analytics, system integration, and cloud, as also traditional services like logistics and marketing.

Third, in societies, individuals are able to leverage new technologies to form new communities as also to avail of services that earlier remained inaccessible to them due to physical distances.

Fourth, these changes have created the new format of individuals as tech-entrepreneurs, with aggregation platforms powered by smart phones emerging as the disruptive business models of the future.

What does all this mean for the Indian industry? Across sectors, India has evolved along parallel paths. One section of the industry is removed from sufficient knowledge and funds to align with emerging technology, continuing to work with conventional resources to meet localized needs. At the other end, India is home to a significant number of the world's largest multinationals, many of them engaging in cutting-edge manufacturing processes. Domestic companies too are competing with the best in the world in terms of productivity and quality, addressing global markets in areas such as automotives, pharmaceuticals, telecommunications, and so on with notable success. Simultaneously, India is emerging as a hotbed of innovation and start-ups in many sectors such as healthcare, financial services, energy and infrastructure. The challenge is to inculcate the Fourth Industrial Revolution processes across a larger proportion of Indian industry.

As this book demonstrates, these processes are gaining traction across several major sectors. While some companies are using 3D printing to meet customer needs, others are using machine intelligence to make their production more efficient. In areas such as healthcare and financial services, new technology is bringing in more users into the consumer base. The examples shared by Pranjal point to an exciting new world that is quickly emerging in the country.

Enjoying a huge base of information technology (IT) engineers and professionals, India has the potential to capture a larger share of this evolving technology-led industrialization market. To consolidate the digital and industrial technology developments and promote India's global leadership role, a holistic policy action is required. This would enable India's software and R&D sectors to extend their footprint in the evolving global industrial revolution, boost India's manufacturing capability for the goods required in the new industrial processes, and enhance India's adaptation of the new industrial processes in its own manufacturing and services sectors.

While India has the capacity to be a global leader, putting the necessary systems in place is crucial. Large-scale investments in a technology backbone will be required to ensure competitiveness – be it robots, sensors and cloud computing for manufacturing, or high-speed connectivity and data pathways for supporting the global services industry, or skilling and building the capabilities of the industry.

Policy must also act to mitigate the threats to Indian manufacturing that arise from the industrial revolution. Such threats include high costs of implementation, data security, lack of trained manpower, and so on. A key issue causing anxiety about the advent of Industry 4.0 is its impact on jobs. In an economy blessed with a large workforce, creation of new livelihoods is essential for development; yet, the new industrial revolution looks for high technology options.

Retraining and upskilling to make the workforce ready for the phenomenon and enabling workers to take advantage of the arising opportunities will be central to the smooth transition to the task of technology adaptation, and India cannot afford to let the industrial revolution bypass its economy.

CII has worked on the issues raised by the Fourth Industrial Revolution and identified five broad pillars to facilitate the intended objectives. The first is building a robust infrastructure to deliver the new business models. This would include digital infrastructure as well as financial infrastructure. The government has stressed both through its flagship Digital India programme and promotion of financial technologies for a less-cash economy. Open-source platforms and technology stacks would be the next infrastructure frontier for maximum coverage. Further, advanced manufacturing such as high-grade semi-conductors, sensors, robotics, and subsystems needs to be promoted.

Access to capital is the second area to prioritize. Small and micro-entrepreneurs are taking advantage of localized solutions but face barriers in finding funding. Criteria for accessing funds from public sources should be made simpler and goal oriented, targeting small and micro-enterprises as well as entrepreneurs. Startup India envisages a fund with a corpus of ₹10,000 crore.

Third, creating an innovation economy requires strong legal protection and adequate incentives for copyrights and patents as an inducement for innovators, scientists, and entrepreneurs. India introduced the new IPR policy in 2016 which aims to strengthen patent offices and laws. The legal framework would also need to focus on cyber security, consumer protection, and a regulatory environment that would best facilitate start-ups and technology adaptation.

Fourth, education and skill training to align the workforce with emerging technology trends is essential. While conventional learning provides a strong foundation, specialized skills courses can be developed to enable learners to continuously upskill and reskill themselves. Just-in-time and needs-aligned training modules should be created, taking employers on board as well.

Further, strengthening research capabilities is the most important pillar for the next-gen technology enablement. Unless India has the most advanced research labs, maintaining innovation advantage will be a challenge. A technology development and deployment fund for 2015-2022, aggregating about ₹1 lakh crore with 60 per cent funding from the private sector, could be a key plank for the strategy. The government also needs to incentivize end-to-end R&D expenditure by Indian companies, from the concept and prototype stage to commercialization and market promotion.

CII has a strong focus on strengthening India's knowledge economy ecosystem, right from 1990 when the national technology committee was set up with Dr APJ Abdul Kalam, India's Missile Man and late President, as its chairman. Our objectives for 2022 include encouraging industry's investments in R&D from the current 0.3 per cent of GDP to the global average of 1.5 per cent by 2020, and also urging the government to increase its R&D expenditure in higher education by ten-fold. We also aim to double the filing of intellectual property by Indian residents and raise the number of post-graduates by five times.

CII with the Government of India has commenced several public-private partnership initiatives for meeting these objectives. The Global Innovation and Technology Alliance (GITA), a not-for-profit company incorporated jointly by CII and the Government of India, manages and implements government's international and national industrial R&D and technology acquisition programmes and funds. The Prime Minister's Fellowship Scheme for Doctoral Research funds PhD scholars for research with funds contributed equally by companies and the government. We are also working with the Council for Scientific and Industrial Research (CSIR) on technology commercialization.

CII is the founding knowledge partner for the Global Innovation Index with the World Economic Forum. Encouraged by India's fast rise in the global rankings, CII is now developing an India Innovation Index to measure innovation in Indian states. Further, we also help bring together corporates with higher education institutes to fund chairs and departments for research. Four Technology Development and Promotion Centers and three IPR facilitation cells have been set up with central and state governments to develop and protect new intellectual property creation.

To take forward the technology depth of Indian manufacturing, we have set up the Smart Manufacturing Council and Smart Manufacturing Alliance to identify challenges and solutions for companies. A sectoral tool has been developed to assess the state of readiness in identified sectors and suggest roadmaps for adoption of technology, apart from other actions.

With these and many other initiatives, we hope that innovation will emerge as a strong component of India's industry engagement.

Pranjal's book uncovers many of the ways in which Indian companies are aligning with technology advance across sectors. The trend is now gathering momentum and we must all work together to accelerate the pace of change in Indian industry so that our country and its industrial ecosystem can be the go-to place for the Fourth Industrial Revolution as it widens across the world. I look forward to the book acting as a catalyst for this process.

Chandrajit Banerjee
Director General
Confederation of Indian Industry

1

INDIA AND THE FOURTH INDUSTRIAL REVOLUTION

Revolutions are not new to India. We have had many over the centuries. Except that none involved the industry. We had social revolutions; green revolutions; many revolutions against our occupiers, especially the British. Some revolutions were local, some regional, and some national. Many social revolutions led to the dismantling of traditional social evils. The green revolution allowed India to feed itself and not starve, as many had predicted it would at the time of Independence. There was also the white revolution that created milk cooperatives, making India a surplus producer of milk.

In Hindi, the word for revolution is *kranti*. It has been associated mainly with India's fight against British occupation, but the word defines revolution at a very grassroots level.

India was strong in ship-building, textiles and steel manufacturing, but a combination of regulatory, tax and policy measures were taken by the British to ensure that these industries suffered and India became dependent on their imports. India missed the industrial revolution on account of British rule.

Most of India's exports were agricultural products, raw materials and minerals. Silk and spices were exported, while most manufactured goods were imported. This continued until India gained Independence.

When industrial manufacturing did revive, it was bound by socialist command economy rules. Till 1991, when economic reforms changed the rules, manufacturers could not expand their production capacity without approval from a mid-level bureaucrat sitting in New Delhi. As a result, widespread investment in contemporary manufacturing technology to suit a growing economy did not happen. It is only in the last twenty-five years that the Indian private sector has begun to adopt technology in their basic manufacturing functions.

Companies across sectors began to actively use technology from the 1990s. Initially, the many joint ventures that occurred between domestic and global companies were solely for technology. In the automobile sector, for instance, the global companies had the technology while their Indian partners had understanding of the local market. The policy environment helped, as there were several sectoral caps on foreign direct investment (FDI). The upshot was Indian companies leveraging foreign technology for the domestic markets. Later, as the FDI caps were relaxed, many joint ventures came apart. Foreign companies like Honda went their way, while local partners, like two-wheeler maker Hero Motors, continued on their own. Over the period of a decade and a half, many smart Indian companies were able to manage without technological partnerships. What they couldn't make themselves, they were able to buy in the global markets.

*

A new kranti is happening in the country now. Another industrial revolution is slowly but surely taking root in India.

This is the Fourth Industrial Revolution, one that consists of a clutch of distinct yet connected technologies that are growing and evolving at a rapid pace. It is impacting almost every aspect of business, social and personal life, thereby creating an Internet-based economy. These technologies include blockchain, artificial intelligence (AI), machine learning, 3D printing, nanotechnology, the Internet of Things (IoT), energy storage, and augmented/virtual reality.

Most of these technologies are not new. AI has been around for decades. The sensor technology that drives IoT has been used extensively for many decades too. What is different about the Fourth Industrial Revolution is the confluence of all these technologies, at a time when connectivity through high-capacity bandwidth and processing power are at very high levels, and are promising to become even faster and more powerful. The defining aspect of the Fourth Industrial Revolution is its pace of change.

Such is the pace that people get used to unthinkable concepts even before they become reality. Many companies have begun adopting different elements of the Fourth Industrial Revolution and deploying them in different aspects of their businesses. Recent changes in mobile and touchscreen technology have made all of us ready for just about any new breakthrough, even as the rate of obsolescence grows. In our minds, 3D printing is a breakthrough technology of yesterday. The use of drones, though not ubiquitous, is considered normal. Countries like India do not legally allow civil use of drones, but hundreds of weddings in India have been shot using drone cameras. Artificial intelligence is driving several business decisions that impact the lives of millions of consumers in India. Sensor technology has become important for many manufacturing units. Neuroscience in now a key tool for understanding consumer behaviour.

Before we delve into how India is embracing the Fourth Industrial Revolution, it is important to understand the previous revolutions. In the pre-industrial age, human strength and ability was the fuel for survival. Early humans foraged, and it took many centuries for them to start farming in an organized manner. Farms allowed humans to give up their nomadic existence and settle in clusters near fertile lands. The domestication of animals created the space for mechanical development.

The First Industrial Revolution was initiated by the invention of the steam engine. Railroads and mechanical production of tools and machines followed. This happened between 1760 and 1840, roughly. The Second Revolution began around the late nineteenth century, with mass production and electricity. The Third was the digital revolution, led by the use of computers. It began early in the last century. The development of mainframes and semiconductors in the 1960s ushered in personal computing, which became ubiquitous in the 1990s. And finally, the Internet set the stage for the Fourth Industrial Revolution.

To better understand all this, let's take a few examples and see how they transformed over the four industrial revolutions. In the pre-industrial age, the key sources of energy were water, air and wind power, and, of course, human effort. In the First Industrial Revolution, coal provided energy, and in the Second Industrial Revolution, oil and gas, along with electricity, which as a form of energy could travel distances. In the Third, renewable sources of energy were added. And in the Fourth, distributed energy systems, marked by huge investment in batteries and storage, will fuel economic activity. Energy will be available through a network of connected storage systems.

Mobility in the pre-industrial revolution was through sail-powered shipping. The First Industrial Revolution saw mechanical navigational aids, steam engines, and large rail and shipping networks. The Second Industrial Revolution saw oil-powered ships, planes and automobiles. The Third Industrial Revolution used satellite-based navigation to aid transportation as opposed to paper maps, while the fourth is ready with autonomous vehicle networks.

In production, too, there has been fast-paced change, from artisanal production to now fully automated robotics. Speed and pace are the critical differentiators between the first three revolutions and the fourth. Each of the previous revolutions took centuries and decades to develop. The fourth is barely a decade old. From keypad phone to touchscreen phones; from touching to gestures; from gestures to neuro-signals – mobile phones have transformed almost to the point where they will no longer need to exist physically; a software alone will allow people to communicate.

Business and political leaders are so aware of this pace of change that few are willing to make a prediction for any change beyond three years. Suddenly, 'disruption' is the word of the decade – much used, much abused and little understood.

With more than fifty billion devices being connected online, issues of cyber-security and data privacy are top on the agenda of policy makers across the world.

This kranti for India has a larger meaning. To coin an acronym, KRANTI is Knowledge, Research, and New Technology in India. Indian industry is now being driven to invest in research and knowledge on how best to grow with these new technologies.

For India, the Fourth Industrial Revolution brings tremendous opportunities to leapfrog many stages of development, hastening its journey towards becoming a developed economy. In many ways, the Fourth Industrial Revolution is a leveller. The technologies being used in India will be the same as those in use in the developed world. Robots, AI, IoT are all technologies transforming industry in the West and are ready to do the same in India. The Confederation of Indian Industry, a body of Indian corporations, is now actively encouraging its members to adopt relevant technologies for business competitiveness. It was a pleasant surprise to discover that most industry leaders had already launched initiatives, pilots, and projects within their organizations.

Among these technologies, it is IoT that can make the biggest impact on Indian industry. In its essence, IoT is a technology system that connects every part of a product lifecycle to an Internet-based platform. Let's take the lifecycle of a ceramic cup. From its design to its raw materials to its manufacture and delivery – every aspect would be connected to its manufacturer's system through the Net. The design would be done on the cloud, and the raw material supply tracked online. Its manufacture in a factory, and the different elements in the factory will be connected. And, so will its delivery. For this to happen there would be sensors to constantly update the relevant data to the management. This would improve the efficiency of product lifecycle management. So far, parts of this cycle are connected online in some companies. But IoT connects every step of the cycle, from design and supply to manufacture and delivery, also making every step of this process visible to the management. This allows for transparency in tracking as well as allowing greater flexibility to the management to make improvements.

This book is an effort to chronicle the changes that the Fourth Industrial Revolution is bringing about in India, and to showcase some of the best examples of how it is playing out in the country. It is impossible to be exhaustive in this effort. Many companies refused to share their experience. Many said it was too early for them to talk about the changes in their organization and functioning. There isn't enough research on the management and structural changes that technology is bringing. Much of the information is anecdotal as companies are evolving to make the most of the new technologies. Most of the cases in the book have been put together with the help of research, interviews, conversations, site visits, and material provided by the companies.

What I discovered was impressive though. India, too, is not shying away from this fourth revolution. A considerable number of companies in the country – domestic, global, family-owned, professional, small, and large – has taken the plunge in one way or another. Companies are adopting different elements of the revolution in diverse ways, some gingerly, some in a sure-footed manner. Many have launched pilot projects, while many others have totally migrated some of their business functions to AI-led processes. And many companies are still waiting and watching. Some have been stunned into inactivity. They don't know where to begin, or how to start deploying the technology all around them. Between the time I began collecting examples and up to the time of completion of my work, many new technologies that were on the fringe became mainstream. In 2016, a talking software – the kind that pops up on the screen and answers queries – called chatbot, was a novel idea for consumer-facing activities. By 2017, hundreds of companies were using interactive chatbot software. In 2018 or later, chatbots may be replaced by something totally new.

Such is the pace of technology that the gap between futuristic apps and yesterday's technology has narrowed to just a few months. The gap could get narrower in the future. What is fantasy and futuristic today will easily be the new normal in a few months', if not weeks' time – not just for consumers, but for corporations too.

For Indian companies, this is a challenge of course. Just when they gear up to adopt a new technology, a better and more efficient version is developed. Companies that will be able to survive in this atmosphere will have to display tremendous agility. Already, there are debates on changing organizational structures. A chief technology officer (CTO) is no longer the person responsible for making the computers work. The CTO is as important on the board as a chief financial officer (CFO) has been. Some companies have created the position of 'Chief Digital Officer' to reflect their change in approach. It is no longer about creating a technology strategy. For boards and CEOs, the talk is now about strategy in a technology-led world. From being the wheels of the organization, technology is now the engine. The choice of engine and its efficiency will define success. New business models created on technology platforms is the new normal.

There is much that India has to be worried about too. An over-reliance on automation will shrink job creation. India has already been through almost a decade of jobless growth. Automation and robotics in industrial manufacturing suits countries with low productive populations. But it does not suit countries like India, where 12–13 million people enter the job market every year. I will dwell on this a little later.

Many companies have increased the level of automation mostly because of cost advantages. Honda Motorcycle and Scooters Company in India is proud of its automation. Its fourth plant in Vithalapur near Ahmedabad has 241 automated processes. Its first one in Manesar, near Delhi, had just 65. The difference in productivity is 36 per cent.[1]

The International Federation of Robotics says the highest volume of sales recorded for robots was in 2015. Sales increased 15 per cent to more than quarter of a million units. The automotive, electronics, and metal sectors are the biggest users of robots. This trend will only intensify in the years to come.

The Fourth Industrial Revolution is in its early stages. It is quietly picking up pace. Purely from the job creation point of view, there are likely to be severe challenges, especially in the matter of reskilling manpower to meet the needs of new technologies. In the three preceding industrial revolutions, there were disruptions at every turn and resistance to every new development. There was progress, there was pain. (But when has progress ever happened without pain.)

The pace of change in the Fourth Industrial Revolution brings with it much uncertainty. What is certain, though, is the need to prepare for and cope with it. Companies have to invest in a constant cycle of training and reskilling. The cost of technology will reduce but the cost of good talent will rise, simply because supply will not meet demand. The effort to keep the demand in sync will require investment in people. When technology becomes a commodity, talented professionals will become a luxury. However, it has now become evident that from the perspective of productivity, efficiency, and consumer focus, the Fourth Industrial Revolution is triggering tremendous benefits for the companies investing in it.

As it happens, India has begun incorporating many a new technology, but has still some way to go to cope with the change. The Fourth Industrial Revolution is recent, and enough research on its impact is not available. But there is enough anecdotal evidence of its potential and advantages. This book is really a chronicle of the changes that are taking place across companies and sectors right now in India.

Broadly speaking, there are three types of technological developments taking place in the Fourth Industrial Revolution.

The first type consists of the innovations that are happening in the West but are being deployed or have the potential to be deployed across the world. These include the sharing economy initiatives, led by Uber and Airbnb.

The second type comprises solutions meant only for local needs. These are low-tech and affordable solutions that work in emerging markets. India's financial inclusion plan using mobile technology is a good example. Such solutions, though very local, can be adopted and adapted by other countries.

The third type is being created in emerging markets but it has the potential to be scaled up across the world. India's Oyo

Hotels is a terrific example of how low-to-middle-level hotels can be connected to provide cheap and efficient hospitality services. Other examples include M-Pesa that originated in Kenya, and WeChat of China. WeChat began as a chat and messaging solution, but is ahead of Silicon Valley products like WhatsApp since it allows payments too.

Digital technology is leading to financial inclusion of millions of Indians. Connected technology is bringing about a revolution in affordable healthcare. In the services sector, consumer needs are being better served with data analytics. This has taken strong root in manufacturing companies too. Data analytics is being used by advertising and marketing companies, and even automobile companies to keep track of consumer behaviour. For marketing, as well as for studying driver behaviour, car companies are using connected devices. Their sales teams are trained on mobile phones, and consumer feedback is received almost instantly. Connected cars are giving real-time information to their makers as well as to insurance companies. A car driver can possibly see his insurance cost reduce if the car offers data about his high-quality driving, and therefore his lower chance of meeting with an accident. Says Guillaume Sicard, the former president of Nissan's India operations, 'Today the need for data and speed is very important, especially in sales and marketing.' His marketing team uses a real-time dashboard on mobile devices. Training updates are sent on mobile devices, while sales trends are instantly captured and analysed.

For capturing the right data, the design of processes has become critical. Harry West, a former Massachusetts Institute of Technology professor is now the CEO of Frog, a design and strategy firm that focuses on Fourth Industrial Revolution technologies. This is what he has to say: 'Around big data, some of the most obvious challenges are of understanding and interpreting. And that's a design question.' In a cyber attack, for instance, vast quantities of data are generated. Similarly, dealing with millions of consumers and recording their behaviour makes for a lot of data too. Companies and organizations are now investing in design to create and capture this data. 'It is important to abstract them in such a way that a human being can understand what is going on very quickly,' says West. He says the idea is to identify patterns, to analyse the root cause (of problems) and to craft an appropriate response. The design, ultimately, will be a human decision. Even if AI plays a role in it, the framework will have to be developed by humans, says West. The design challenge, and making sense of data for human-centric response, is a critical and difficult challenge.

However, there is a gap in some sectors. While some technologies have become popular, others have not. India hasn't embraced digital currency yet. According to financial information website *MarketWatch*, digital currencies are worth $100 billion now. Bitcoin accounts for more than half of this, but there are other popular cryptocurrencies too. These include Ethereum, with a 28 per cent share of the entire cryptocurrency market cap, and Ripple with an 11 per cent share.[2] More than 800 cryptocurrencies are listed with *Coindesk.com*, a digital currency information resource.

Cryptocurrencies are based on blockchain technology. This technology is simple in its concept. Each 'block' is a packet of digital data that is constantly updated and secured. This block can move between entities and individuals without the need for constant verification. The information carried in this block is secure and authentic. In some ways, it is like a currency note that can't be copied and is trusted by everyone. In the same way that a user of a currency note does not verify each note with a central bank, the blocks are trusted by all parties in a transaction. In the financial sector, transactions are carried out through intermediaries who verify an instrument. Without intermediaries and their verification of instruments, transactions are not accepted.

Consider this. When we write a cheque, we have to give it to an intermediary (the bank) for verification and processing. But when we pay cash to someone we don't need an intermediary. Blockchain is the digital version of currency notes. With blockchain technology, intermediaries are not needed. This will have a profound impact on banks in the coming years. Not surprisingly, the most popular form of blockchain are crypto or digital currencies like Bitcoin. Blockchain technology is being used to develop many more applications too.

This kind of technology could further transform how financial services are delivered in India. It can be used to tailor specific financial solutions that can service millions. Peter Smith, co-founder of the company Blockchain (named after the technology), a digital wallet provider and software developer, feels that developing countries will benefit in many ways from this technology. 'For me the most interesting application is probably around identity because that's where everything has to start from,' Smith told me at the Web Summit in Lisbon, while referring to developing countries like India.

The distributed ledger system or independent packets of software of blockchain can allow development of products precisely tailored to individuals.

In mobility, app-based car services like Uber and Ola are already commonplace in India. Both companies have been aggressively growing and competing in the country. The future, though, will be more than just personal mobility. For such companies, entry into logistics is the next big step. In India, Uber Eats has already been launched and is being expanded. This is a food delivery app that was rolled out in the US and Europe earlier. For Uber, delivering products is as important as delivering people. Uber Freight, along with other companies, has begun experimenting with self-driving trucks. Uber doesn't differentiate too much between regions like Asia or Africa when it thinks up innovative ideas. 'Now, what is clear is that there are a lot of opportunities to use technology to continue to make the experience better for users, riders and drivers. There is a lot of innovation indeed in the field of machine learning and things like that, that we apply across the world,' Pierre-Dimitri Gore-Coty, head of EMEA – Europe, Middle East and Africa – at Uber, told me.

'We have to adapt to different countries and we have had to make sure that it (our service) fits the population that we're trying to sell to,' he said. One clear example of that is the use of cash in certain markets like India and Brazil. Uber allows cash options in these countries where credit card usage is limited, but not in other countries. 'It's something that three years ago at Uber would not have been conceivable, so we have had to adapt on that front,' Pierre said.

For Uber, a service that depends entirely on public cellular bandwidth availability, ensuring quality of service is a big challenge. Here too, many innovative solutions have been created. 'We're also trying to adapt to low wire network bandwidth, so how do you make the app and how do you offer people the ability to access the Uber app with poor data coverage, and with limited bandwidth. And we keep working on ways like that to make the expense as local and suited to the local market as it can be. We have product teams that are specifically focused on places like India and East Africa. There are teams which are always trying to tweak and localize the product so that it better fits the population and the cities we're trying to sell in,' said Gore-Coty.

Companies dependent on technology solutions do not see countries as separate markets. They see countries as different configurations of challenges. This makes almost all countries equal. A car-riding solution in the US and East Africa will be similar. Only the approach to delivery of the solution will be different.

India is also in a good position to provide space technology for the Fourth Industrial Revolution. Since the Internet of Things will need connectivity across the country, the Indian Space Research Organization (ISRO) is offering access to remote locations through the NAVIC system. Navigation with India Constellation or NAVIC is a system of satellites that are self-reliant in position, navigation, and timing services. This set of seven satellites will reduce dependency on foreign satellites and will improve the quality and speed of information. Chairman of ISRO A. S. Kiran Kumar told me in an interview,

'We have a messaging system in navigation which can reach out to any remote place in the country with low communication linkages. Internet of Things which require many switching activities to be done at very remote place will be effective using our technology.'

In health tech, small companies are making a global impact. The advances in gene editing, for instance, will be deployed across all countries including India. I met Rachel Haurwitz, president and CEO of Caribous Biosciences, a Berkley-based firm. It is four-year-old company that is developing a technology called CRISPR, which enables scientists to precisely change DNA sequences within cells. 'We look very broadly at the applications of this technology. From new therapeutics to agricultural applications. From industrial bio-processing to basic research. We work with other companies to deploy gene editing in their product development cycle. We have worked with Novartis on drug discovery. With Dupont Pioneer on gene editing for plant breeding. There is tremendous potential for this technology to transform human health. Gene editing can also be used to fight various types of cancer,' Haurwitz told me. Such applications will be eagerly deployed by healthcare companies in India. Most of the healthcare companies are using connected technologies with a focus on smart hardware for affordable solutions. Most of them don't focus on research and development the way Caribous does. However, Indian companies are well placed to consider deploying such cutting-edge technologies like CRISPR for fighting cancer and related diseases in India.

*

At the global level, the Fourth Industrial Revolution charge is being led by the US and Germany. In the US, the lead was taken by GE when it announced the 'Industrial Internet platform' in 2013. It has brought together other like-minded technology companies to jointly develop solutions for the global markets.[3]

With Intel, IBM, SAP and Schneider Electric, GE founded the Industrial Internet Consortium for joint and coordinated efforts in this area. Large-scale industrial and manufacturing projects would be managed through cloud computing. From concept to design to manufacture, assembly and delivery, every step would happen using platforms created on cloud computing.[4]

Similarly, Germany initiated its Industrie 4.0 as part of the country's government strategy for enhancing its focus on future technologies.[5]

Germany launched the Plattform Industrie 4.0 in 2013 in Hanover as part of its 'Action Plan High-tech Strategy 2020'. Government bodies, chambers of industry and technology leaders like Siemens are driving the coordinated developments on this strategy. This effort has gone beyond Germany to Europe and to other emerging markets like India through the G20 countries.[6]

Examples of the work done by GE and Siemens are detailed later in the book. Both these companies have innovated and deployed technologies for their Indian operations.

*

There is a natural fear of job loss resulting from automation and robotics in India. Repetitive processes are being increasingly automated. Banks in India are already using chatbots and even humanoid robots. A Kannada-speaking robot in Canara Bank in Bengaluru will direct you to the right counter. HDFC Bank has the Ira robot, which helps customers choose the right service and financial products. In an *Economic Times* report, the CEO of Asimov Robotics that developed Ira is anticipating increased demand from many banks.[7]

To be sure, the tasks done by these robots are basic. In some ways, they are only offering answers to Frequently Asked Questions (FAQs). But as robots become more sophisticated they will increasingly replace humans at their jobs.

There are several projections for job losses owing to factors such as automation and consolidation in the market. While 12–13 million graduates and engineers seek jobs every year in India, the country is expected to lose 1.5 million jobs annually too.[8] A report by PeopleStrong says, one in four job losses in India will happen on account of automation.[9]

In the IT sector, more than 2,00,000 engineers will lose their jobs, says another report by Head Hunters India.[10] The argument against automation and robotics, therefore, sounds very strong. There is no question that efforts to reduce costs and increase efficiency will lead to reduction of people at corporations and institutes. The much-discussed solution to reskill people and build stronger industry-academia linkages are important too, to mitigate the impact.

However, there is the other argument that gets lost in the debate on job losses. Let's consider, for instance, a situation where companies in India do not adopt automation, robotics or AI. What happens then? Over time these companies will become inefficient and are likely to get pushed out of the market by smarter global entrants. In an open economy, it will be tough to argue for keeping out competition.

In many ways, companies in India are ensuring their survival by adopting these technologies. Those who adopt faster and better will be more competitive than others, and definitely in a better position to compete with global entrants. Their survival comes at the cost of jobs. But these can be countered by reskilling, and by creating new opportunities.

The use of data analytics is opening up efficiencies in sectors like agriculture that did not exist earlier. Cargill India, for instance, is allowing thousands of traders to be part of the system by using mobile-based pricing data. The entire value chain from farm to fork can provide livelihood to hundreds of thousands of people who may not have formal skills but are ready to share their understanding with the help of mobile connectivity. The Fourth Industrial Revolution in India has taken root and is spreading fast. While some kinds of employment in some sectors will suffer, others will gain. The focus for industry and for policy makers is to create programmes that allow the educated unemployed to find ways of benefiting from this kranti.

The number of unique mobile connections in the world will cross 5 billion in 2017, and approach 5.7 billion by 2020, says industry body GSMA. India and China will account for more than half of this number. India will get another 370 million users by 2020.[11]

The use of mobile phones will create livelihoods and work for people in ways that may be difficult to imagine today. A report by Promatics suggests that the mobile app economy will be worth more than $130 billion by 2021.[12] And the emerging markets like India will lead the way. Another report says India is already the fourth largest app economy.[13]

In a conversation with Prime Minister Narendra Modi in June 2017, Tim Cook, the CEO of Apple, said that apps have created jobs in India. Cook said more than 7,50,000 jobs here can be attributed to apps on the Apple IoS platform. Indian developers have created 1,00,000 apps; registering a growth of 57 per cent over 2016.[14]

New industry sectors are being created. These have potential to create work for millions. There is already an industry association for producing and promoting the use of drones in India. The Unmanned & Autonomous Vehicular Association of India (UAVAI) is a collection of companies that wants the government to create an environment of growth in this field. Its vision is, 'India builds unmanned and autonomous vehicles for the whole world.' UAVAI wants to use such vehicles or drones in every possible function of public and corporate life. The government is working on a policy framework, since civilian and commercial use of drones is not yet allowed in India. Some start-ups have already begun to produce and assemble drones in the country. The work and employment impact of this technology is difficult to predict, but clearly India could need an army of professionals to build and manage the use of drones across different sectors.[15]

The jobs of the future will be determined by the spread of the Fourth Industrial Revolution. The jobs that are currently at highest risk of redundancy have been studied at Oxford University. In order of risk, the jobs are those of telemarketer, loan officer, cashier, para-legal and legal assistant, taxi driver, and fast food cook.[16]

WEF's *Future of Jobs* study predicts that 5 million such jobs will be lost to robotics and AI, among other technologies.[17]

So far only one job has been eliminated by automation, according to a Harvard paper. Out of the 270 listed jobs in the US census, the occupation of the elevator operator has been totally wiped out during the period from 1950 up to the present.[18]

But there is also a list of jobs of the future. These jobs will require cognitive skills, systems skills, complex problem-solving, content-generation, and social skills. So software developers, marketing professionals, and management analysts will be in demand.[19]

And of course, new jobs that do not even exist today could come up, such as those of robotics veterinarian, holoportation specialist, and climate engineer.[20]

The Fourth Industrial Revolution will transform the very concept of work. Earning a living will move from traditional permanent jobs to contractual work and self-employment. Organizations will offer project-based work for which temporary teams will be created and paid. Once the project is over, the team will be disengaged. Though this approach has been around, now it will become the norm. India is already in the midst of a start-up renaissance. As the impact of technology drives down jobs in certain sectors, skilled people will become entrepreneurs, self-employed, and contribute to the sharing economy outside of the framework of nine-to-five jobs. Between 2015 and 2016, more than $13 billion has been invested in start-ups in India. This trend will only gather momentum.[21]

Prime Minister Narendra Modi launched the Make in India campaign in 2014 to promote job creation and manufacturing in India. Since then the concept has spread to the service sectors too. The Fourth Industrial Revolution will play a critical role in this campaign. Policy makers in the Modi government have the tough task of anticipating change in a rapidly changing technological environment and making relevant policies. Here rapid reaction will help, since change is unpredictable in many ways. What is sure though is the need for large-scale diversion of manpower from tradition roles and jobs to new ones that may not even exist yet. Jobs will be created, but Indians have to know how to prepare for them.

India needs a collaborative effort like Germany and US to foster Fourth Industrial Revolution. The collaboration will promote and encourage development of technologies for domestic solutions. The effort would aggressively look for ways to mitigate the impact of employment. Within the kranti effort, Indian industry and the government will have to invest in new technologies and platforms. It will have to create a long term ecosystem that trains and educates professionals. India could collaborate with the US, Germany, and the EU. The central government can consider a joint platform between ministries, state governments and industry bodies to create a mission for making the most of the Fourth Industrial Revolution technologies.

*

The curious aspect of the Fourth Industrial Revolution in India is that it is not being led by the fabled information technology industry. The leaders in that industry have been so caught up with business process outsourcing and manpower-heavy enterprise solutions that most of them have not been able to adapt to technologies like AI, machine learning, IoT, and blockchain. These technologies are estimated to account for less than 10 per cent – some would say less than 5 per cent – of the revenues of these companies.

To be fair to them, they are trying hard.

'Digital inclusion means saving one rhino, one drone at a time,' said a flyer shared by TCS at the Davos summit in 2017. Another one read, 'Digital Inclusion means not losing the crop to blight.' Tata Sons chairman, N. Chandrasekaran, and TCS CEO, Rajesh Gopinathan, spoke about the industry increasingly offering solutions based on IoT.

The then Infosys CEO, Vishal Sikka, led discussions on the subject with other global leaders. An invite to business leaders by Infosys at Davos 2017 read, 'We are transitioning into a truly digital future, one that is being shaped by the decision-making capabilities enabled by AI and automation technologies.'

Wipro organized a debate at Davos 2017 on how technology will enable responsive leadership to mitigate the negative impact of automation while offering new opportunities to citizens. At Davos Wipro event, delegates could experience new technologies through HoloLens, a head mounted display that allows viewers to view products in 3D. Rishad Premji, chief strategy officer and a member of the board, told me that Wipro is increasingly focusing on artificial intelligence and machine-learning-based solutions for its clients worldwide. 'Wipro HOLMES is designed with a focus on enterprise use cases from IT and business process areas; (it) has the ability to continuously learn from new data, recommend a solution and predict failures,' the company website promises its clients.[22]

For Indian technology companies, this is new language. For decades, they had created and worked a successful business model based on cost arbitration and coding solutions. As the Fourth Industrial Revolution manifests itself across the world, the three leading Indian technology companies are presenting a new face to global clients.

Gopinathan says that the Digital Empowers campaign of TCS is about using technology for solving the challenges faced by society and not just for corporate needs.

At Infosys, the focus is on its new automation platform Nia (earlier Mana), which means purpose in Swahili. 'We want to bring purposeful AI to enterprise,' Sikka had said, at the launch of Nia in April 2017. 'AI can be much more than what automates work.' Companies like Johnson Controls say Infosys is helping them build leading-edge automation capabilities.

At Wipro, the Holmes platform is already delivering AI and machine-learning solutions to Indian and global clients. Several banks and financial institutions have begun deploying Holmes for customer-centric and back-end processes.

A report done by industry body Nasscom with KPMG says, fintech software will be a $45 billion market globally by 2020.[23]

For Indian tech companies, this and other opportunities are the new goals. Other segments that are becoming key markets include 3D printing, cyber security, data analytics, augmented reality, and new applications of virtual reality.

Smart marketing and repositioning are the key words for these industry leaders. But a lot of this marketing effort is being done to compensate for the fact that these companies have been slow to establish their presence in AI and IoT. The problem with the IT leaders in India is that a very small percentage of their business is focused on the Fourth Industrial Revolution. The CEO of a global IT company from India laughed at the very mention of the term Fourth Industrial Revolution. 'If you can understand what it is, please tell me too,' he said, mocking the idea itself. This was as recent as in 2016. While global technology companies have moved rapidly to AI and IoT, the large Indian IT companies have not been agile enough. Most of their work is still focused on coding and troubleshooting. 'Indian IT firms started out as custom software houses. They created a unique delivery model where 75 per cent of the work could be done in India using low-cost but highly skilled computer scientists. This task is increasingly done by machines using AI, thereby not requiring the high volume of engineers,' said Vijay Govindarajan, Coxe distinguished professor at Tuck Dartmouth College's Tuck School of Business.[24]

Not surprisingly, growth for the Indian IT sector is now on a downward curve. Despite the rapid adoption of technology across every sector, the Indian IT companies are not in a position to offer solutions on the scale that the market demands. Industry body NASSCOM has the figures to confirm this decline of the Indian IT sector. It had projected export growth of 10–12 per cent in 2016–17, but exports grew only 8.3 per cent, to $117 billion. For 2017–18, NASSCOM has projected a flat growth of 7–8 per cent in exports and 10–11 per cent in domestic business. Compare this with an exports growth of about 17 per cent and domestic market growth of 20 per cent in 2010–11, and one gets the complete picture.[25]

While the industry blames protectionism for its lacklustre growth, a large part of its problems is due to its inability to adapt to the needs of the Fourth Industrial Revolution. Former chairman of Microsoft India and director on the board of Infosys, Ravi Venkatesan, is scathing in his assessment of the industry. He says the IT industry in India is facing its Kodak moment of becoming obsolete. 'India's IT companies are struggling to navigate a tectonic industry shift. Its leaders have seen the technological and regulatory shifts coming for the last decade. They have recognized the limits of wage arbitrage and understood the need to shift from renting IQ to creating IP, and becoming more global. They see the giant new opportunities afforded by the digital revolution. But as the story of Kodak shows, seeing is not enough. Acting decisively and forcefully is crucial,' he wrote in the *Times of India*.[26]

A new class of start-ups in the country is focusing on the Fourth Industrial Revolution, but they still have some ground to cover. The interesting part is that the mid-level IT companies in India have been more agile and responsive to technology changes.

Global technology companies and local mid-level IT companies are leading the Fourth Industrial Revolution in India. In the next few years, the size of revenues and staff will not be as relevant as the companies' ability to harness new tools for corporate solutions. Employment in Indian IT is slowing sharply. From new job creation of 2,30,000 annually, the figure has dropped to 1,50,000. Plus, many companies are reducing their number of employees as automation in coding is picking up in India. In 2017, about 40 lakh were employed in IT/ITES by Indian companies. But the mid-level techies are likely to become redundant since their jobs involve activities that can be automated (planning, scheduling, allocation, forecasting, etc.). However, the industry is still a net hirer as loss of employment in some sectors is likely to be offset by hiring in sectors such as machine learning (ML) and fintech. Disruption in the next few years will come from start-ups, while big firms might try to capitalize on the developments through acquisition, integration, and expansion.

A big market for such companies will lie with the government, which would want to improve delivery of basic services. The focus on financial inclusion and Digital India is a key part of that intention. The government is working with IndiaStack, a 'set of APIs [application programming interface] that allows governments, businesses, start-ups, and developers to utilize an unique digital infrastructure to solve India's problems towards presence-less, paperless, and cashless service delivery.'[27]

IndiaStack works primarily on these services: Aadhaar authentication, eKYC, UPI, eSign (where an Aadhaar cardholder can digitally sign a document instead of needing to print it out to sign it physically), and digital lockers.

It appears that the technology revolution in India is being led by non-infotech companies. That's not a bad idea since it reflects a deeper and wider spread of the Fourth Industrial Revolution. The next few chapters cover some exciting examples across logistics, the consumer sector, financial services, hospitality, travel, energy, manufacturing, and agriculture. Consumers living in small towns in India appear to be equally open to adopting wearables and apps as those in the megalopolises. The 900-million-plus mobile users in India are keen on picking up new ideas.

Armed with smartphones, Indians are more tech-savvy than ever before. Take a look at these Google statistics for India.

- India is in the #2 place globally for mobile search queries (the US leads).

- Search is now in nine languages on desktop. In India 10 per cent of all searches are Indic searches.
- Indic Keyboard: Launched in 11 languages in December 2014, it has been downloaded over 10 million times.
- Amongst YouTube's (YT) top 10 countries worldwide, India is one of the fastest growing – both in terms of total Watch Time (WT) and mobile WT.
- In India, YT Watch Time grew over 230 per cent YOY (year-on-year) in the fourth quarter in 2016 on mobile devices (Mobile + Tablets).
- In India, over 80 per cent of YT Watch Time is spent on mobile devices (Mobile + Tablets) – (Q4-16).

These changes have transformed not just the media sector but have also brought elements of the Fourth Industrial Revolution, like AI, to every mobile.

Few people realize that when the Gmail app on a smartphone readies an answer to an email with options like 'let me see', 'I'll check them out', or 'thanks a lot for sharing', it is AI that has determined the pattern of customer preference and prepared a customized option.

Consumers are already living with AI and ML. And now the demand for talent that can help the industry in these fields is rising. Tech HR company Belong says the demand for IoT talent rose 304 per cent between 2014 and 2017. Belong has created Talent Supply Index, a first-of-its-kind index that measures emerging roles in technology and related sectors. According to Belong's Talent Supply Index for June 2017, there is a big supply and demand gap. 'Demand vastly outstrips supply for core AI, IoT and Cloud talent: Data Scientists, Devops Engineers, Security Engineers ... hiring will continue to be a struggle for tech companies in emerging technologies,' said Belong TSI.[28]

This is the big shift. The old technology of previous industrial revolutions had moving parts. The new technologies control the moving parts. So far India has created many infotech companies but not pure technology companies. New start-ups promise to go beyond IT and grow into technology companies.

Thus, the industry is now investing in talent and trying to catch up with consumer and client demands. The fifty or so examples in this book demonstrate how they are doing so.

2

MANUFACTURING

Suman Bose is an evangelist. And he is not too shy of admitting he is one. The former managing director and CEO of Siemens Industry Software India speaks passionately about the positive impact of technology on society and the economy. Ask him about how robots and automation are killing jobs across the world, and he scoffs at the suggestion. Whenever he gets a chance to address a large gathering of industry leaders and professionals, he firmly attacks the view that automation and machines are hurting the economy. A story he loves to share is about washing machines and women in the US.

'When washing machines became popular in the US in the 1920s, it saved a lot of time for women. They could get their household work done faster. Not surprisingly, they soon had more time on their hands,' Bose says. In the decades following the advent of household machines, women could stay away from home longer and they joined the workforce.

A study by the University of Montreal says that technology liberated women. 'These innovations changed the lives of women,' says Prof. Emanuela Cardia, Department of Economics, who presented the study in 2009.[1] 'Although it wasn't a revolution per se, the arrival of this technology in households had an important impact on the workforce and the economy.'

Prof. Cardia based her research on more than 3,000 censuses conducted between 1940 and 1950, from thousands of American households, across urban and rural areas. 'We calculated that women who loaded their stove with coal saved 30 minutes every day with an electric stove,' says Cardia. 'The result is that women flooded the workforce. In 1900, five per cent of married women had jobs. In 1980, that number jumped to 51 per cent.' In 1913, the vacuum cleaner became available, in 1916 it was the washing machine, in 1918 the refrigerator, in 1947 the freezer, and in 1973 the microwave. All of these technologies had an impact on home life, but none had a stronger impact than did running water.

Bose says such studies show that new technology has helped the economy and society over the years. Siemens is now working with global and Indian companies to improve technology to produce smarter machines in the cleverest of ways. 'Cyber-physical systems are changing the way machines are made and used,' he says.

Let's try to understand what this means. Simply put, it means the entire process of production as well as delivery is connected through a technology platform. The cyber-physical is a dimension of the IoT where every single process, component, and system is connected on a relevant platform.

This may seem obvious, but it is not so. Take the example of a car maker. There are several steps in the manufacture of a car. From concept to design to manufacture to delivery, there are different functions for which there are different teams and companies at work. While this applies to the car itself, it is equally applicable to all its components. A single car has over 30,000 components. Each of the components and sub-systems is made by different companies. One component is made and embedded in a larger one. These together form a sub-system like the steering wheel. The sub-systems then get fixed with a larger system, which then combines with another, and so on until all of them are put together on an assembly line as a single unit, the car, and rolled out of the assembly line.

All this requires tremendous planning and coordination. While each company playing its part has a software that connects its internal organization and manufacturing, this software is not necessarily connected with those of other parts makers or the final car maker.

In the IoT framework, every single component will be connected to others and to the final car through an elaborate network, from concept and design to final delivery and usage. The use of sensors on raw materials and components means that each piece that goes into the car carries information about itself that can be tracked and monitored at all times. Imagine trying to manage hundreds of students of a school group in a crowded amusement park. A connected system will allow constant monitoring of who is where and doing what. Similarly, a manufacturer can monitor every stage of every component and its assembly through the information carried by the component. The product itself becomes an active part of the production process.

The life-cycle of a typical component or product consists of design, production planning, production engineering, production execution and finally, services like delivery, etc. Companies like Siemens now offer solutions that enable a manufacturer to place the entire production life-cycle on a common, connected platform.

The advantages are immense.

Experts like Bose believe that integrating product and production life-cycles can reduce time to market by 50 per cent. Effectively, this means that, planned properly, a manufacturer can conceptualize, make, and bring a new product to a consumer in half the time taken earlier. This is a significant advancement, since high levels of technology obsolescence and fast-changing consumer tastes can be satiated by rapid creation of new products.

Another advantage is higher flexibility in manufacturing. If the product design has to be changed or some elements have to be amended, the connected system can react instantly and respond appropriately. And in the end the system allows high levels of efficiency not just in terms of time but in the use of resources too.

*

The earliest known manufacturing units used slave labour and animals. Manufacturing was characterized by slow production, lack of standardization, and variable output. Strength and stamina were preferred to intelligence when it came to hiring employees.

Eventually, with the First Industrial Revolution, production facilities became bigger. The earliest non-life-powered facility is supposed to be the Derby Silk Mill in England (estd. 1721), which used a water wheel for working its machines. Machines were especially useful where: a) manual production time was high (such as in smithys or mills), or, b) where there was a need to exert greater force than was manually possible (forges).

With the invention of electricity, it was possible to situate factories without being restricted by the availability of natural resources. This led to the creation of urban centres, affecting both the balance of power and the social structures of their host locations, and to reduced entry barriers for workers and cost of retention for employers.

War-time efforts resulted in improvements in production techniques, statistical models for quality control, and understanding and application of material sciences. From heavy machinery (tanks, armoured vehicles, ships, and big guns) to small items (ammunition, clothing, tins for storing food, firing pins, screws, etc.), both design and production changed drastically. In a manner of speaking, the Second World War was fought between the German and the American industrial engines.

For a world still reeling from the effects of the World War, factories offered employment opportunities to millions of people along with the satisfaction that they were contributing towards rebuilding their nations. By the 1960s, almost everything that had a demand in the market could be mass-produced. Equipment could be designed and deployed for any purpose.

Companies, always on the lookout for cheaper solutions, fine-tuned their processes until they could reduce their costs no further. The focus then shifted to replacing manual labour – which was both expensive and slow, not to mention entailing ancillary costs like pension and healthcare, as expected of a benevolent employer – with machines that could work 24x7, tirelessly, repetitively, and without any loss of accuracy.

In fact, robotics had been around, at least as a distant possibility in manufacturing, since 1937, when Griffith P. Taylor demonstrated a simplistic grabbing-and-stacking machine. In 1956, Unimation became the first company to produce robots for industrial applications. Their earliest models could transfer objects only a short distance, but it was a revolutionary step for the time – a proof of concept that in time there would be machines to run other machines. The idea of a completely-automated production plant was no longer the stuff of incredible sci-fi.

ABB Robotics and KUKA Robots were soon competing with Unimation – who had by then upgraded their own designs to increase the range of movement of their models – in Europe. In the years approaching the turn of the century, there was a distinct separation of approaches to robotics. While both European and Japanese firms continued to vie for primacy among industrial applications of robotics, the Japanese had taken lead in the mass-market sector, where robots were used as 'assistants' in civilian homes.

In addition to speed, improvements in manufacturing have also contributed to growth in production of electronic goods on a massive scale. Microchips are produced in the millions, each unit insulated from dust and environmental corruption, thanks to sterile units and automated fitting and vaccum-sealed packing. Humans have already been reduced to mere spectators.

Nano-technology has also altered the landscape dramatically. Essentially, we now use machines to produce smaller machines of the order of nano-meters. Since nano-tech is being applied for critical applications where safety and hygiene are of paramount importance (for instance, in medical surgery or environmental operations such as cleaning up oil spills), even the hitherto acceptable standards of failure are no longer acceptable!

Archaic labour laws, a reluctance to embrace manufacturing, and lack of governmental support (not to mention protectionist laws, opaque rules, and rampant corruption) have, until recent years, discouraged manufacturers from setting up plants in India. While domestic companies like MRF eventually grabbed the lion's share of the world's market, there had never been a concerted effort to make India a manufacturing hub. Ever since the days of the British Raj, India had been relegated to being a source for raw materials and a dumping ground for finished goods.

Even after Maruti Suzuki, arguably one of India's most efficient manufacturers of its time, was started, waiting times were high for its products, running into months on end. Even for two-wheelers, the situation was the same. Despite the high (almost prohibitive) costs of ownership, people were queuing up to place orders for their Javas, Lambrettas, Chetaks, and 800s. One of the major reasons for this backlog was that even though the rest of the world had moved to computer-aided manufacturing and production lines, Indian industries were still at the mercy of labour unions who would usually oppose every move to modernize plants and processes, arguing that this would inevitably result in retrenchment of hundreds or thousands of loyal workers. In many cases, this was a pyrrhic victory for the unions – they would win concessions only to drive the company itself bankrupt, its output and sales now inadequate in the light of its new commitments to the workers.

Since globalization in the early '90s and the reforms on the License Raj afterwards, manufacturing in India did indeed become relatively easier, despite the red-tape bureaucracy that still called the shots.

Inevitably, given that the objection labour unions would raise over automation and the absence of alternatives (or spare parts) if valuable equipment broke down, many companies figured it would be cheaper to work with manual labour instead of using costly, high-maintenance machinery. There were other systemic issues that helped perpetuate this attitude – production machinery would inevitably have to be imported into the country, their clearance subjected to the prevailing laws, and the mood of the customs and duty officers. On top of that government permissions were notoriously hard to get.

Of late, though, there is a realization that India needs to manufacture more if it has to keep up its pace (sustainably) of consumption. Blackberry and Apple have already agreed to manufacture their models in India instead of in China or any other nation in the bloc simply because the key decision-makers are Indians.

Relaxation of import barriers, knowledge- and technology-transfer, foreign investments, special measures by the central and state governments, are helping India catch up. The new plants that come up are designed to be as 'future-proof' as possible, but sometimes political one-upmanship takes its toll on the very section of the population that would have benefited from these investments.

The three elements to manufacturing are the following:

First, there is the overall production design to planning the life-cycle of a product. Within this, there are components that include use of technologies like automation, robotics, and 3D printing. Of course, 3D printing, also called additive manufacturing, can be part of the traditional production life-cycle and can also be a totally self-sufficient system for creating products. Companies have to adopt technology to integrate all elements and processes. Something that even the government has to consider while making policy.

The present government's #MakeInIndia campaign has given a huge fillip to the cause of manufacturing in India. Until now, the sector had suffered because it offered a middling solution no one needed. Indian production was not as cheap as China's, but on the other hand, the quality of a typical finished product, generally speaking, rarely met Western expectations. Through the new campaign, the government has finally given direction to the industry: the focus must be on quality.

Siemens Cyber Physical World

Siemens has been helping companies to adopt technology for transforming their processes.

Matrix Tools and Solutions (Matrix) works with some of the world's largest original equipment manufacturers (OEMs) to develop products and tooling. The company's products and services include product design, die-casting dies, injection moulds, thermo-forming tools, compression moulds and jigs, fixtures and trimming tools. Matrix is a one-stop shop for product development, handling all phases of the process, from concept to design, engineering, validation, manufacturing and production.

Headquartered in Pune, India, the company operates a design lab staffed by highly talented designers, and a mould-and-die manufacturing facility equipped with advanced machine tools for producing and assembling mould-and-die components. Matrix also offers batch and mass production of zinc and aluminum-cast components, produced in two plants for cold- and hot-chamber processing. Its clients include the Tatas, Varroc, Huff India, John Deere, and Magneti Marelli.

Initially, Matrix was using 2D computer-aided design (CAD) software for product design. With the 2D approach, it was difficult to re-use design data, even for minor changes, and there were many errors requiring small but time-consuming manual changes that could compromise quality and delivery schedules. To address these issues, Matrix sought a 3D CAD solution, evaluating and trying several alternative systems, but most of them lacked satisfactory capabilities for tool, mould and die design.

Matrix chose Siemens NX Software suite to replace the traditional, two-dimensional way of doing things. The 3D visualization allowed it to plan the tools and products in much sharper way than previously possible. An almost virtual-reality view ensured that small changes were easier and faster. With an extensive library of components and robust handling of different formats, it is not really surprising that NX could help the company in reducing costs and shortening delivery times.

✶

Kirloskar Brothers Adopt 3D Printing

A heartening part of the adoption of the Fourth Industrial Revolution is how traditional and family-run businesses have warmed to it. Companies like Marico, Raymond, and Kirloskar Brothers are eagerly adopting new technologies under progressive leadership.

Sanjay Kirloskar, the affable and soft-spoken chairman and managing director of Kirloskar Brothers Ltd. (KBL) is steadily transforming his factories. Pune-based KBL is the flagship company of the $2.1 billion Kirloskar Group. KBL engineers and manufactures industrial, agricultural, and domestic pumps, valves and hydro turbines. It was established in 1888 and incorporated in 1920. KBL has eight factories in India, and packaging and manufacturing units in countries in Asia, Europe, and Africa. The group's focus on advanced technology has been ingrained for generations. Sanjay's grandfather S. L. Kirloskar was among the first Indians to graduate from Massachusetts Institute of Technology as a mechanical engineer.

Sanjay has been an advocate of new technologies and has acquired European companies to stay ahead of competition. He has been the first in his sector to adopt additive manufacturing (AM) or 3D printing in his pump factories in India.

The conventional method of manufacturing needs patterns to produce the castings of pump components, which is not only time consuming but also labour-intensive. To accelerate the new product development process, AM technique is being used at the Kirloskarvadi plant. The 3D sand printer machine is among the largest in the world and is used to prove new development concepts and help bring innovation quickly to the market. The printers are used for research and development activities with respect to pumps, valves, and turbine component casting and manufacturing process in the foundry. This technology is used in foundries to print the mould and core directly, without any patterns for components like impellers, bowls, diffusers, and volute casings for which moulds and cores are quite complex.

Moulds and cores are prepared based on 3D models (CAD data) and use sand and resin chemicals to bind the layer-by-layer printing. This technology saves the time taken for manufacture of the pattern equipment as well as the material machining process. The design process is iterative. During each iteration process, it involves manufacturing, materials and time. KBL says it has reduced the time of development along with reducing man-hours, machining time, and material content. Though there are significant time gains, the cost of printing compared with the conventional method is very high because of the smaller sieve of sand and machine consumables. KBL is working on a balance that can ensure that the higher cost of 3D printing can be balanced with higher productivity and a reduced end price.

Since other pump makers in the world are also moving to such technologies, KBL is taking efforts to stay a step ahead of competition.

Even IoT plays a role at KBL. The water facilities at the Kirloskarvadi plant are run with a remote management system. The distance between the HQ at Pune and Kirloskarvadi is 200 km but the plant's water system is remotely monitored and managed from the HQ. The software that runs the system minimizes breakdown, creates alerts, and ensures that water is available to the plant and the small township of 1,800 residents at Kirloskarvadi.

*

Raymond: Tech That Works Like Heaven

One of the oldest manufacturing companies in India, ninety-year old Raymond is increasingly using new technology in its factories. Technology plays a very crucial role in the textile sector, especially when it comes to the textile manufacturing business. 'Robotics, big data, and material science technologies have already been adopted by Raymond partially and are proving to be a boon for our product development so far,' says Harish Chatterjee at Raymond.

'Raymond has always been ahead of the game when it comes to adopting advanced technology. The company was the first in the textile sector to introduce ERP (enterprise resource planning) software by SAP in its organization.' Raymond also uses the TOC (theory of constraints) principle to manage its inventory and production. This theory breaks down all systems into a series of constraints that need to be overcome. Its software works on this to reduce lead time for manufacturing by about 25 per cent. In manufacturing, Raymond uses software on looms that keeps account of key parameters each and every second.

The company employs 30,000 workers in their sixteen factories across the country. The company is using robotic manufacturing that will reduce reliance on workers over time. One robotic process can replace 100 workers. These workers can then be deployed in service-oriented roles if required. While robotics is important, it will be balanced with use of labour.

'You have got to balance technology with labour and costs. A lot of robotics is happening in China. We have looked at robotics but it doesn't make financial sense. The capital investment to labour employment ratio in our sector is very high. So, for a ₹100 crore investment we will take 5,000 people, but in steel, a five times higher investment will need only one-tenth the workforce,' says chairman Gautam Singhania.[2]

Singhania is bullish about the range of technology-infused fabrics called TechnoSmart that he has introduced. The fabrics in this range allow for UV protection and are more resilient. The branding here is smart but the manufacturing process is where the real application of technology is taking place.

He adds, 'Dyeing is a fully automated process. When you mix colours, it has to be very precise to the last thousandth of a gram for shade matching. For this, human intervention is not possible. If you want that consistency of quality. Technology can be used in multiple ways. Technology can be used for monitoring. Data will tell me how efficient my plants are.'

In the new manufacturing plant at Amravati in Maharashtra, Singhania is gunning for efficiency and quality as machines become faster and better. 'The spinning technology has changed. The finishing technology has changed. So the finishing person is investing in technology to give you the one per cent more. The spinning person is giving one per cent. The weaving person is giving one per cent. But together, they bring ten per cent better quality and efficiency!'

*

Sensor Systems of Marico

Another traditional company that has embraced technology in manufacturing is Marico Industries. The $900 million personal care products company is using new technology for traditional products. Founder and chairman, Harsh Mariwala, is focused on deploying new systems in old processes.

'There are some early adopters, primarily within the industrial sector in India. However, I think the sector is still at a nascent stage currently. At the thinking level, the ideas have started to flow. Some prototypes and early adoptions are under way. Hence it is poised to rapidly grow in the next two-three years once the early prototypes start becoming successful,' says Mariwala.

'Manufacturing companies are putting sensors in their plants to gather data pertaining to productivity and downtime planning. Companies have also started to control energy consumption, not only in factories but also in offices, with HVAC and smart energy solutions,' Mariwala says. He is implementing some in Marico's manufacturing units.

Marico has been piloting sensor-based systems along with SCADA systems in two of its plants in order to capture manufacturing information on a real-time basis, which leads to real-time production diagnostics (RTPD). The data collected on this basis is fed on to a new information and intelligence platform (which will then be used for better analytics in order to predict and improve plant performance and also to improve asset effectiveness). In addition, Marico is exploring wearable solutions to gather information about its consumers' hair and skin health. Using this knowledge and its current products, the company can help provide a 'service' solution to its consumers. In some ways, Marico is implementing the cyber-physical system that Suman Bose talks about. Not only is the entire process of manufacturing connected, the feedback from consumers will be also be looped into the system.

According to Mariwala, India contributes to 75 per cent of the company revenues. Their technology and R&D departments are also situated in India. Hence the work done in India is at a higher plane than the company's work in other countries.

Marico has invested in an analytics platform with the necessary columnar databases, Extract-Transform-Load (ETL) tools as well as a visual analytics front end. Marico is using Tableau to provide descriptive analytics solutions in the areas of sales, marketing, and supply chain with very good results. It has significantly reduced the time taken to make and gather data for further analysis. It has also undertaken predictive analytics projects in the areas of sales, procurement, supply chain, and marketing. Some of these projects have been completed and have given good initial results. Marico believes that analytics in the areas of consumer behaviour and engagement, online sales behaviour analysis, and retailer analytics will add significantly to its competitive advantage in the near future.

As an Indian FMCG company, Marico Limited is in the health, beauty, and wellness space. It operates primarily in the emerging markets of Asia and Africa.

In 2014, Marico decided that 'What got them here, won't get them where they wanted to go'. It called out an aspirational growth for the future and identified five 'transformation areas' where it had to undergo change to make itself future-ready. These were:

- Innovation,
- Go-to-market,
- Talent value proposition and culture,
- IT and analytics,
- Value management.

In a statement to me, Saugata Gupta, MD and CEO of Marico had said, 'It is not just a one year or a quarterly milestone. What we are doing is making the organization Future Ready in predictable, repeatable ways.'

Marico says it has always been an IT savvy organization. In the early-to-mid-2000s it had not only implemented a big SAP ERP project, but had also connected all its major distributor customers through a distributor management system (DMS). The sales personnel were given hand-helds (much before mobile became a buzzword) to ease their field work.

With all this data available with Marico, it wanted to harness the opportunities presented by digital and analytics in order to gain further competitive advantage.

With better Internet bandwidth in the country, and lower cloud computing and data storage costs, Marico could now bring all its customers' bill-wise, item-wise, daily data onto a central platform. It set up an analytics stack called MUSIX (Marico Unified System for Information Exchange) comprising columnar databases, ETL tools, and the descriptive visual analytics of Tableau.

This helped improve data visibility and bring about a single version of truth across functions – sales and marketing, supply chain, and finance. It saved more than 40 man-days per month across functions, enabling its managers to release their valuable bandwidth and improve focus in order to make better decisions. The improved reviews helped generate better sales through focus on the right areas in the October-December 2016 quarter, which was affected by the demonetization in India. The volume-growth results were better than that of its competitors for that quarter.

It also extended this analytics and automation capability to the planning and forecasting system, using predictive analytics-led logic along with order automation systems. The forecasting accuracy increased from an average of 65 per cent to 78 per cent. The predictive analytics in R language helped improve the sales assortment mix sold to the retailers. This helped increase sales by 16 per cent versus the control sample. The logic was fine-tuned and is planned to be extended to over twenty cities in the calendar year 2017. Better analytics also led to improved market mix modelling and effectiveness of sales spends. Called Project Edge internally, the technology drive helped improve effectiveness of spends by 5 to 7 per cent, which was traditionally a holy cow and never questioned. For distributors, there was the advantage of faster delivery of products.

Mukesh Kriplani, chief of business process transformation and IT at Marico, says the changes became important because of the rapid growth of Marico with acquisitions and new products.

Marico acquired Paras Pharmaceuticals around three years ago and was now in the chemist and cosmetics category that was new to the group. Moreover, its food products such as Saffola had shown high growth.

To manage different ranges of products, consumers, and geographies, Marico has relied on technology to predict its distribution and sales patterns for effective inventory management.

Marico is implementing a 'sales assortment mix analytics' model to help the company predict selling and buying patterns across similar territories.

'We know, for instance, that consumers in the Pali Hill area buy certain kinds of products. Consumers in Jubilee Hills in Hyderabad may have similar buying patterns. The analytics model will be able to suggest if SKUs that sell in Pali Hill area can also be sold in Jubilee Hills. If it's a 'yes', then you have cracked a new SKU and increased your reach,' says Kriplani.[3] This model is in the pilot phase. Marico has rolled it out in a South Indian city and is encouraged by the results.

The next step was for Marico to focus its efforts on its factories. It increased the number of sensors installed to monitor various parameters across the production chain. Over 400-plus sensors were installed in two of its factories to initiate the project on IoT. The sensors were installed across energy meters, flow meters, temperature and pressure gauges, RPM sensors, level transmitters, and visual flow sensing devices. The data is pulled in from these various sources and through SCADA, SAP, and dot net portals, and collated into a manufacturing intelligence information system in SAP. This has allowed Marico to drive real-time production diagnostics (RTPD). This in turn is helping improve operational equipment effectiveness (OEE) as well as energy efficiency across these factories. Once stabilized, it will be extended gradually to all factories in the future.

Marico wants to double its sales in the next few years. And further acquisitions by it cannot be ruled out. For such goals, an analytics and IoT-based foundation has been laid already.

*

GE: Digital Models and 3D Prints

Among the most exciting uses of the Fourth Industrial Revolution are the projects being led by GE India. The multi-sector company has a presence in India across sectors like aviation, transportation, medical systems, and energy. In all its efforts, it has now aggressively included the elements of artificial intelligence and additive manufacturing (or 3D printing).

GE calls itself the world's digital industrial company, transforming industry with software-defined machines and solutions that are connected, responsive, and predictive. It seeks to combine the industrial power of its past with the software brains of future. Industrial Internet is the integration of industrial machinery (what we call 'big iron') with cloud-based analytics ('big data'). Simply put, it is the marriage of minds and machines. It is building machines that are predictive, reactive, social, and better able to communicate with other machines and customers. Equipped with innovative software, data analytics and sensors, GE's machines continually generate intelligence to enable its customers to keep airplanes on time, prevent power outages, improve patient care, better manage natural resources, deliver sustainable energy, and produce billions in operational efficiencies and costs savings. GE's goal is to deliver better outcomes for its customers through digitalization.

GE Digital is playing an integral role in GE's quest to become the world's best digital industrial company. There are three elements to its strategy, which involves the entire GE organization: GE for GE; GE for our customers; GE for the world.

GE for GE: It is making machines smarter and being smarter about what can be done with them. It is creating systems that manage the entire industrial ecosystem, from design to installation to service and beyond: this is the digital thread. Today the daily data volume is about 10,000 TB a day, and in 2020, it will increase to millions of terabytes each day globally.[4]

GE for our customers: GE businesses are creating the applications built around their customers' systems and processes. Not just the machines, but the entire asset portfolio, so it can deliver the best outcomes. These are aimed at generating outcomes – for example, a wind farm can generate 20 per cent additional electricity when optimized.

GE for the world: The cloud is the future of computing. It is scalable, secure, and cost-effective, which is why it GE has built Predix, its cloud platform created specifically to manage industrial data. The company has opened it for general availability.

GE offers products in key areas that industrial companies use to manage their assets and operations more efficiently. They are Predix, Asset Performance Management (APM), Brilliant Manufacturing, Automation, and Security. GE says Predix is the world's first and only cloud-based operating system built exclusively for industry and is the foundation for everything. Predix is not only an enabler to the business – it is the business. With more than 20,500 developers on the platform, GE, its partners and customers are already using Predix to build software and applications for the industrial Internet. Its 300-

plus partners with thousands of certifications are driving share and helping build the app economy.

From being a manufacturing company, GE is now as much a software company, given its focus on the industrial Internet. It boasts more than 20,000 software professionals across its businesses worldwide. Since 2012, GE has invested more than $1 billion in software. By 2020, GE expects to be a top-ten software company and have more than $15 billion in software and solutions. By 2020, 10,000 gas turbines, 68,000 jet engines, more than 100 million light bulbs, and 152 million cars will be connected to the Internet. And GE hopes to be at the centre of this industrial web.

The key concept that is driving GE's efforts is called digital twin. Built on GE's Predix platform, digital twin refers to the software model of physical assets. The Bangalore team based at the John F. Welch Technology Centre (JFWTC) leads digital twin capability development. There are 1,76,000 digital twins running at the JFWTC today, and GE expects exponential growth in that number. The digital twins are assets at the component, product, and system level. Digital twins can help predict the remaining life of an asset, recommend maintenance based on the estimated remaining useful life of the asset, and recommend the best maintenance work scope.

In simplest terms, digital twin is the virtual model of any product, component or system. Before manufacturing begins, the team builds its digital twin and tests every aspect and every situation. Once the testing is final, the product is built. This ensures that the time cycle of building physical prototypes, testing them, and rebuilding them is significantly reduced.

Consider GE's experience using digital twin in wind forecasting for renewable energy in India.

GE has been working with Indian wind customers to help them implement the mandate that all wind farms should provide forecasting and scheduling of power to their grid operators. In 2014, it partnered with a customer, Panama Wind Energy, to demonstrate a proof of concept for their wind farm in Maharashtra. The farm was already running a wind-forecasting solution but it was not able to provide the level of forecast accuracy needed. For this pilot, they made available two months of historical data, and GE used analytics to provide them better predictions. After piloting it for several months, in 2015, GE productized this as a digital twin of a wind turbine. The solution accounts for current performance data from the turbine as well as for other parameters in the wind farm to make accurate predictions.

Its wind forecasting solution demonstrated 94–97 per cent accuracy as compared with the industry leader's accuracy range of 80 per cent to 86 per cent. GE's self-learning algorithms provide better accuracy and therefore lower penalties for wind operators. They are part of a complete analytics package integrated with the digital wind farm. Their pay-for-performance pricing model is aligned with customer outcomes. This solution is adaptable, can provide a 30–360-minute look-ahead and eight to sixteen updates per day.

GE says it does not just offer a solution, but by using digital twins guarantees outcomes for its customers. The solution is now being deployed across the globe and there is interest in North America and other APAC countries as well.

This is a fundamental change in the way business is done in the wind energy sector. Earlier GE would only sell its customers the physical assets but now it is partnering with them to deliver their outcomes too.

The deployment of such models speaks highly of GE's belief in India as a centre for research and development.

GE is now going to build 1,000 locomotives for Indian Railways, building about 100 every year. The first batch is scheduled to be out by 2018. The full design, which was put together at the Bangalore centre, has been created only for Indian Railways and is not a copy of an existing design. GE has an engineering team of close to 200. The factory in Pune will make some of the components, while bulk of the manufacturing will be done in the two new factories in Bihar. So the manufacture of the locomotive will entirely happen in India.

A digital thread will be created for the entire process; it would perhaps be the first time the concept is used in India. 'Digital thread' means the entire process will be created digitally so there is data available at every step of the way. GE has done away with drawings. This locomotive has been fully designed and manufactured in 3D. The digital process allows the engineers to look at all the manufacturing data and all the supply-chain data, from suppliers, vendors, and in-house. They will then improve the functioning and productivity with deep learning algorithms, or machine learning algorithms. The digital thread will ensure data for every component and process so that later engineers know where to intervene to improve something or to rectify an error.

Let's take a look at what role additive manufacturing will play. For the various components of the locomotive, the engineers will build 3D printed models for testing. The virtual models will be rendered into physical shape with 3D printing for a shorter testing time cycle. These 3D printed prototypes will help the company to understand functionalities, the function performance, etc. GE is using additives to help understand the design and to get the right design in place.

In the next few years, components made by 3D printers will not just be used for testing but would also be installed in the locomotive. Currently, for the locomotive manufacturing for GE in Bihar, elements of additive technology are being used for the design, and at the concept stage. Soon the additively manufactured components could be supplied for actual use in the locomotives.

Banmali Agrawala, the then President and CEO of GE in South Asia, was justifiably proud. 'We have the opportunity to leapfrog from basic low-end manufacturing, fabrication, etc. to 3D manufacturing, 3D metal printing, additive manufacturing. It is a lot more efficient, it is a lot more cost-effective, and it is a lot more cerebral.'

The process of manufacturing has changed in India already. 'The other dimension is industry 4.0 which is along digitization. So, you will not find any drawings on the shop floor. No drawings! It all comes digital. With digital twin you can simulate, you can mould, you can foresee what's happening. So, you know predictively what might go wrong with that machine, when do I need to change, and so on and so forth,' Agrawala had said.

In many ways, GE in India is ahead of the company's operations in many other countries. GE is doing the digitization bit in stages. It has a few 3D printers in India and is using it for plastics, for prototypes. The next step will be metal 3D printing. 'So, the game changing thing is going to be additive manufacturing. Because in additive manufacturing we completely eliminate any constraints in design,' Agrawala said.

*

Such a modern approach to manufacturing is not the only innovation GE is into these days, nor is it true that GE is the only firm that's banking big on new-gen solutions such as the one listed above. Raymond, for instance, is making its textile mills and its products smarter, while other companies like Marico are leaving no stone unturned in getting the best that today's (or, in some cases, even tomorrow's) technology has to offer in making their businesses more efficient and the quality of their products or services as perfect as can be.

It is not the attitude that is new, but the technologies and the outcomes that are. The manufacturing world has always been synonymous with the term 'industry', which is understandable, since it was the demands of mass manufacturing that led to the First Industrial Revolution and is, in a way, responsible for all the developments that have been spawned from it.

Something that has always remained constant in the manufacturer's quest is the focus on productivity, on greater output with fewer errors. Given the high volumes and economics of scale, expensive technology hasn't always been automatically shunned – so long as it could pay for itself in the long run, any and every method was feasible and worth exploring. Unlike many other industries, the world of manufacturing has always been eager for change, almost devilishly so. It has sought to appropriate the best discoveries and inventions in the race to make things quicker, better, and cheaper.

*

Honeywell's Software and Hardware Solutions

Global companies in India have been aggressive in introducing automation technologies. While most consumers don't get to experience it, automation has been part of business operations for decades in India. Honeywell-owned firm UOP started operations in India when it contributed to the setting up of the Digboi Refinery in the 1930s. Since such times, India's oil and manufacturing sector has been using automation in some measure.

In India, Honeywell offers automation and security solutions, materials technology, and home and building technology. It has a division for aerospace too. Honeywell is a unique company in that it is equally proficient in software solutions as it is in the hardware that would go with it. This technology and manufacturing firm has allowed many companies in India to use elements of the Fourth Industrial Revolution technology as they realized how deeply important this would be in the future.

'Our chairman has often said we want to be the Apple of the industrials. We believe there will be two types of technology companies in the future: The first that offer cyber-solutions, and the second that will work for the first type. We are becoming a premier software-industrial company globally, and are here to support Digital India. We have an unmatched ability to combine advanced software with great physical products to provide value to our customers across a wide variety of verticals,' says Vikas Chadha, president, Honeywell India, in an interview to me. 'In the Internet of Things, we have the unique advantage of being on the "things" side as much as on the "Internet" or software side. We understand that what we finally sell to the customer is the software or firm-ware that comes with an engineering hardware,' Chadha says.

Thousands of Honeywell products in large industrial establishments give it the advantage of ready access to big data. More than half its global 23,000 engineers are focused on developing software, and its 'connected' offerings are transforming how we live, travel, and work every day. About 8,000 of these 23,000 global engineers are in India.

The best example of how Honeywell has offered a connected solution to a company is the Jamnagar plant for Reliance Industries.

Honeywell Connected Plant

Its 'connected plant' conversation with one of the largest industrial facilities in the world – the Reliance Jamnagar refinery – started in the year 2010.

Honeywell studied with them, for them, the current set of technologies and tools available at Reliance, how those tools are used, and how people are equipped to use those tools. Honeywell works with refineries around the world and, therefore, brings a deep and wide understanding of benchmarks in global refining practices. With that collaborative gap analysis emerged data of about 500 legacy systems that were manual, across 120 plants, twenty-four hours a day. The objective was to connect different departments and operators across the enterprise for real-time analytics, keeping the operator at the core of the drive. Honeywell discovered thirty-five standard operations the operators needed, and completely digitized them. Today, when a shift is over, the next shift manager has access to all of the prior shift's data. Digitizing the operations was the first step.

The second step was to challenge the process itself. Was the current set of processes most optimized for plant efficiency? Honeywell decided to create a role-based library or a dashboard of KPIs. With changes to the work flow, it collects data at every process level. Then it cleans the data, displays the data, and finally makes decisions based on analysis of that data. The supervisor, the plant head, the refinery head, or the head of all refineries then have access to a different dashboard tailored to their requirement. They can drill down to any KPI that is off-mark and make real-time interventions. Not only does the KPI dashboard cover Honeywell solutions, it also covers non-Honeywell assets. For the assets that were not open-protocol, Honeywell asked vendors to open them up.

Reliance and Honeywell Process Solutions developed a manufacturing information intelligence system (MIIS) to eliminate as many manual systems as possible and to go fully digital in functional areas such as operations, maintenance, reliability, and safety. Other MIIS objectives were improved enterprise connectivity, increased real-time analytics and enhanced collaboration by oil and gas, and chemical staffs that historically didn't interact much or exchange best practices.

Reliance and Honeywell went to all six sites and 120 plants over about six months and found they had about 500 legacy systems. Next, a reference architecture was developed, which showed just thirty-five standard operations applications could update all product movement, blending, historian, creation of alerts/alarms, and other functions. Then, the areas most in need of digital transformation were identified, including material transfers in health, safety, environmental and fire (HSEF) areas, manufacturing operations, reliability engineering and maintenance (REAM), and other automation and energy applications. It took about two-and-a-half years to implement the thirty-five applications, which were completed in 2013.

This MIIS project also allowed implementation of other common controls and historian equipment, establishment of better network connectivity, the slotting of generated data into the right contexts for the best analysis, and enabling of better decisions and actions. This lets each user see the performance and context they need, which improved operations management and operator competency. It even integrated Honeywell and non-Honeywell solutions that did not want to talk to each other.

It also improved connections between the 120 plants, Reliance headquarters, and centres of excellence (CoEs) that focus on roughly fifteen technical disciplines. This allowed the polypropylene CoE to get data from its applicable plants and applications, and let the crude oil CoE get its data from the right refineries. The CoEs can also drill down to more detailed applications and equipment and collaborate much more easily.

Likewise, the Reliance process engineering department can use a process monitoring engine built into MIIS, and if KPIs aren't performing right, then they can drill down even to plant schematics if needed, and find and fix what's out of range. Previously, equipment monitoring and performance information were on spreadsheets published once a month, but now tools like Honeywell's Uniformance Asset Sentinel software can check performance once an hour and make adjustments on the fly.

*

Automation may not be new to India but it is rapidly becoming the norm in manufacturing. The real efficiencies will accrue from cyber-physical systems, digital design-based factories, and additive manufacturing or 3D printing. While this technology adoption is limited to a few leading companies today, falling costs could drive their adoption in medium and small companies too.

3

LOGISTICS AND SERVICES

The Muscle Bots of GreyOrange

It is no longer the stuff of fantasy.

In a warehouse in India, racks filled with packets move around a large hall seemingly on their own. On closer inspection, you see they are actually riding on orange boxes on wheels. Hundreds of boxes, in fact, are in sight, criss-crossing the floor, avoiding each other as they transport packets and racks from deep inside the storage rooms to the front end in time for a pick-up or a delivery.

This is the new warehouse that India is beginning to see, not as a one-off but as a trend. These boxes on wheels with a mind of their own are robots that help pack and pick thousands of products in large warehouses. Controlled and driven by pre-programmed software, the robots are guided by warehouse workers for specific tasks. These robots reduce time, improve space utilization, and reduce errors, ensuring that deliveries to consumers are faster and more accurate. A young company called GreyOrange is pioneering these robots in India.

In 2011, two students, Samay Kohli and Akash Gupta, indulged their interest in robotics by launching GreyOrange to bring automation in warehousing for the Indian logistics sector. GreyOrange describes itself as an Indian multinational robotics firm that designs, manufactures, and deploys advanced robotics systems for automation at distribution and fulfilment centres to solve operational inefficiencies in warehouses operated by third party logistics companies, or by companies with their in-house logistics functions.

GreyOrange has grown from a two-man team into a multinational company, expanding rapidly across the Asia-Pacific region, including Hong Kong, Singapore, and Japan. The company today has more than 350 employees, of whom more than 200 work in research and development.

The company believes that there is a strong case for automation even in a country with abundant and cheap manual labour. Manual solutions are ineffective for handling large order fulfilment in an e-commerce age. After talking to e-commerce businesses like Flipkart and Snapdeal, the founders believe that there are five major drivers that should help companies like GreyOrange carve a sizeable market for themselves even as they transform the traditional way of doing things. These drivers are:

- Growth in orders and output in line with the exponential growth of e-commerce and third-party logistics providers.
- The constant need to reduce the turnaround time of an order.
- Seasonal or even promotion-driven spikes in demand and the subsequent increase in product traffic.

- Better inventory management systems to cut down on leakages and other costs, thereby increasing efficiency and security.
- Higher expectations, both from the companies that dispatch goods and from the customers who receive them. This is a sentiment echoed both by observers and other members of the industry.

Typically, the manpower-intensive warehouses have recruited and released employees as they needed. Between training the new hires, making sure they maintain operational efficiencies, and reducing (or at least maintaining a low) error rate, the managerial oversight required is tremendous. In such a labour-intensive environment, the accumulation and deployment of manpower is itself a risky proposition.

Throwing more people into the mix is not a long-term solution, for obvious reasons. Warehouses have limited room for movement, and each additional human on the floor reduces the space available for free movement. Hire too many, and you may find yourself operating a storage space where people, let alone goods, can barely move.

An average human picker in a warehouse is set targets of 172 items an hour, writes Kohli of GreyOrange.[1] This is harmful to the human picker. But anything less is not productive for the company. The solution then lies in partial or full automation. The Butler system (the orange box on wheels) can reportedly pick up 360 items an hour at a minimum. 'While robots may indeed lead to the loss of these jobs, the creation of new roles for engineers, software operators, and technicians means the future of robotic warehouses certainly looks bright, not just for profit-minded managers, but also for warehouse workers who can now work in better conditions,' Kohli says.

GreyOrange is working for leading firms like Flipkart, Jabong, and the Mahindra group. But what GreyOrange is doing for its India clients is not too different from what Amazon is deploying in its own warehouses.

Take a look at the work that GreyOrange has done for Aramex, an international mail delivery and logistics services company headquartered in Dubai, United Arab Emirates (UAE). Aramex employs more than 13,900 people in over 354 locations across 60 countries, and has a strong alliance network with a worldwide presence. Aramex started operations in India in 1997. It has twelve distribution hubs and delivers to 8,000 pin codes across India.

According to Grand View Research, third-party logistics market (3PL) will be about $925 billion by 2020. The exponential growth in the e-commerce domain, proliferation of omni-channel fulfilment, and the transition from pallet-picking to case-picking and piece-picking are impacting the global 3PL industry.

Rapid expansion in the e-commerce segment has been one of the largest drivers of growth for Aramex in India. In fact, logistics is one of the most critical factors for the success of any e-commerce company in managing its business criticalities and retaining its customers. Their solid growth presented several supply-chain distribution challenges to Aramex. The company would charge e-commerce players based on the dead weight of sample shipments, but would be charged by the carriers (air or road) on the basis of the volumetric weight of every shipment. This was resulting in significant revenue leakage for

Aramex. Further, it was under tremendous pressure to meet the stringent service-level agreements defined by various customers and to deliver shipments to extremely tight schedules. Sorting thousands of packets of varying sizes and shape efficiently in a few hours and in the limited transit centre spaces was extremely challenging for Aramex. Also, manual sortation till the last-mile (pin codes) was error-prone, with errors in the range of 3 per cent to 5 per cent daily. Managing the surge in demand during the festive season further added to the complexity of the problem for Aramex.

Aramex selected GreyOrange as its partner to leverage next-generation warehousing technology solutions to resolve the multiple challenges it faced in order profiling, sorting, and routing.

To enable Aramex to optimize its billing processes to improve revenue recognition, GreyOrange installed a profiler solution comprising a manual scanner system, a dimensioning and weighing system (DWS), and a rejection arm with an output of 1,500 packets an hour at its Delhi hub. GreyOrange DWS is capable of accurately calculating both the dead weight and volumetric weight of shipments, and measuring the packet dimensions and calculating real volume and box volume, helping Aramex to charge its customers appropriately for shipments without any revenue leakages. The GreyOrange profiler performs at a 99.9 per cent accuracy rate, and has a 24x7 global customer support.

As the load at the Aramex Delhi hub increased manifold in a few months, GreyOrange upgraded the manual scanner system in the profiler to an automated scanner system, which enhanced the output of the system to 3,000 packets an hour.

The automated scanner is additionally capable of capturing and archiving images of order shipments. This automated volumetric data collection and archived images of packets also helped Aramex reduce pilferage. It also helped in auditing the charging policy based on both the images and volumetric weights of the shipments.

As Aramex's business grew in scale, it also faced challenges with the sortation process in sorting really high volumes, and single-item orders of different shapes and sizes that needed to be shipped to numerous pin codes across India. To handle this challenge, GreyOrange expanded the existing profiler to the GreyOrange linear sorter, which was capable of profiling and sorting 3,000 packets an hour. A challenge that GreyOrange overcame in expanding the existing solution was non-availability of space. The profiler was installed on just 1,500 sq. ft. of the floor area. GreyOrange worked together with Aramex to add another 1,500 sq. ft. of space, which was previously being used for non-core activities, to install the GreyOrange linear sorter in a super-squeezed facility with almost 90 per cent space utilization. The GreyOrange sorter helped Aramex scale up its operations by consolidating distribution into one hub and still meet the demand of the entire Delhi region. This resulted in significant cost savings for Aramex. Also, Aramex was able to manage its business growth without increasing the size of the hub.

The GreyOrange PPTL system, a proprietary technology, allowed Aramex to efficiently further sub-sort the packets even up to the last mile (pin code) levels, with minimal errors. The sorter management software also enabled Aramex to create configuration profiles for defining sortation logic for both inbound and outbound processes, allowing quick switching from one profile to another in minutes, while significantly reducing sortation time for shipments. GreyOrange's solution enabled Aramex to achieve the required output, while effectively utilizing the space in its hubs. Aramex scaled up operations from 4,000 to 8,000 to 20,000 shipments a day – and even 25,000 shipments a day during the peak season – by leveraging GreyOrange linear sorter. Aramex was able to consolidate operations at five sortation hubs into one central, fully automated hub, thereby reducing costs by 50 per cent. There were negligible errors in sortation as there was minimal manual intervention. For the company, the serviceable pin codes rose by almost three times.

To summarize Aramex's gains, its operating expenditure reduced by half while space utilization improved. The turnaround time rose by 40 per cent, and gave it the ability to process shipments in just a few hours.

This provided an opportunity for Aramex to expand its customer base in India. It also allowed Aramex to handle peak loads during the festive season. GreyOrange assisted Aramex in defining a barcode template for the shipments coming to it, helping it streamline its processes. Before implementing the GreyOrange solution, Aramex used to manually map airway bills (AWB) for any shipment to a pin code and sort the packets based on the destinations, making it a really long, tedious and error-prone process. GreyOrange's solution also solved the data-integration challenge by automating the process of mapping AWB numbers to pin codes, reducing the error-rates associated with the manual processing. As a result of the tremendous success in Delhi, Aramex replicated the model for the Mumbai region, as output requirements for Mumbai were also on the rise.

Aramex installed the GreyOrange linear sorter with an output of 3,000 packets an hour in Mumbai. This resulted in Aramex consolidating its operations in the Mumbai region too, while realizing substantial cost savings. Aramex also installed the GreyOrange profiler at its Hyderabad hub.

'Manual sortation was error-prone, errors in the range of 3 per cent to 5 per cent daily. With the GreyOrange sorting solution, we have a 100 per cent accuracy rate. So as long as the client has given us the right pin code, the packages reach the end destination, without any further sorting from the origin to the destination,' says Percy Avari, regional manager, South Asia, Aramex.

The advantages that appeared exceptional are now rapidly becoming the industry standard.

*

Perhaps no other business function has evolved in all its aspects – form, output, reach, execution, and basics – as logistics has over the centuries. At one point of time, logistics was essentially sending your goods with a prayer through a trusted (if you were fortunate enough to have such a choice) associate. Now, just the way transportation talks about last-mile connectivity, logistics talks about last-minute visibility.

Trade through the ages has centred on logistics. Merchants loaded goods that were plenty on their shores and dispatched them to far-off lands through mules, caravans and ships, and waited anxiously for the returning consignments that would consist of valuable currency and/or goods that could be sold locally for a profit.

It wasn't just trade that thrived on logistics, though. Entire armies roamed the surface of the earth on the back of robust supply lines that kept them connected to their home kingdoms, bringing forth men, weapons and food, and sending back the spoils of their successes. Genghis Khan's campaigns spanned over 6,000 kms from his kingdom, and it was only when his supply lines were at risk of overstretching and snapping that he chose to return. In the Second World War, the siege of Stalingrad and the breakdown of German logistics were instrumental in turning the tide of the war in favour of the Allies.

Like finance, logistics too has been at the forefront of adopting technology to make life easier. In the post-war years, with massive reconstruction projects going on around the world and businesses scaling up their international operations, logistics became an essential function for companies. The unification of Europe, the standardization of shipping rules across the continent and the rest of the Western world, the explosive jump in consumer demand for goods, and the developments in transport technology – bigger ships, faster aircraft, and sturdier trucks – transformed logistics from being a mere function of production to a discipline of its own. Third-party logistics is now an industry by itself, commanding more than $850 billion in 2016–17 and expected to cross the trillion-dollar mark in another six to seven years.

Until recently, the growth of this industry could be allied very closely to developments in the transport industry. Super-tankers, super-trucks, and super-planes are now common sights on many international routes, bringing economies of scale to the movement of goods from one place to another. Even within these modes of transport, there have been considerable improvements, such as cold chains, freezers, climate-controlled/self-powered containers, etc.

The level of real-time information that we are used to today would not have been possible without the emergence of a new paradigm in mobile/satellite communications. The Global Positioning System (GPS), originally envisaged as NAVSTAR for Pentagon's use in military applications, was opened up for civilian use in the 1980s. Although an open system in principle, the controls imposed on GPS by the US government has led to other countries/groups starting their own versions, such as Russia's GLONASS, China's BeiDou, Europe's Galileo, and India's IRNSS.

Software development has kept pace with advancements in hardware and is now at a point where a user can remotely monitor a GPS-enabled entity from anywhere in the world. Fleet management has thus become much simpler for logistics firms that work across large geographies, relying on incontrovertible, machine-provided data instead of human-provided information. It is not just the service providers themselves who can track the journey of their shipments from the first mile to the last; the advent of Internet technologies has now enabled even the clients to access data specific to their orders, allowing them to view on computer screens where, down to a ten-foot radius, their cargo is in real-time. The level of precision demanded and provided in logistics is among the highest in any industry.

The key areas of focus in recent years for R&D in logistics appear to be at the very ends of the chain – the source and the destination. Near-Field Communication (NFC) and Radio-

Frequency Identification (RFID) systems are now being deployed at warehouses and outlets to keep track of their stocks' quantity and quality. Retail operations are now more closely allied with logistics than ever before, relying on shelf-mounted (Walmart) and point-of-sale scanners to automatically order and schedule deliveries. UPS, DHL, and FedEx, some of the biggest TPL companies in the world today, are continuously working on reducing their time-to-transport (TTT) by using analytics to schedule pickups, dispatches, and deliveries.

Vendors of such solutions also swear that such measures reduce losses from theft, damage (in transit or storage), and pilferage; their clients seem to affirm this by continuing to adopt their solutions.

The possibilities, it seems, are endless; out-of-the-box thinking is no longer a rarity because the box itself seems to be dissolving around the world. A town in Belgium, Bruges, built a two-mile pipeline from an industrial region to the historic centre of the town to transport beer from breweries higher up on the hills, reducing the carbon footprint of trucks, and the accompanying wear and tear of roads

Innovation and experiments in last-mile delivery of products have been picking up pace. While the Bruges example appears whimsical, it does underline how smart engineering has allowed a city to preserve itself while sticking true to the logistics' profession's most sacred value – safe, undamaged, and on-demand-on-time services.

At one end is the hyper loop system being developed by Elon Musk. In this system, underground vacuum tubes will push capsules filled with people or cargo at hyper speed. This is not as impractical as it sounds. The pilot project will be ready in a few months. Another experiment that is becoming mainstream is the use of drones to deliver packages right to the customer's doorstep. Companies like Amazon are already using drones for last-mile connectivity.

The impact of 3D printing is being felt too. 3D printers can convert almost every place into a manufacturing unit. For the logistics industry, this could become a nightmare. The current system is built on sending products from a large production base to multiple sales locations. With 3D, there could be a proliferation of small production bases, each eager to ship its produce to several markets. The logistics industry would thus have to manage far more complex connections than it does today. On-demand manufacturing will create fresh challenges for the industry. Such technology will be popular in countries like India, where high population density reduces the space available for large factories.

*

DHL: Augmented Reality Redefines Logistics

Global logistics companies like DHL are pioneering new ways of monitoring and delivering goods. In a survey done by DHL in 2015, customers identified five priorities: fast delivery, product variety and availability, enhanced search functionality, flexible delivery options, and easy return and exchange.

Of these five, four are driven by logistics. And this is why technology-empowered logistics is becoming critical to every company that has a product to manufacture and sell.

The latest technology being deployed by companies like DHL is augmented reality (AR). Warehousing operations account for about 20 per cent of all logistics costs. The task of picking the right product from within the giant warehouses is as much as 50 per cent to 65 per cent of warehousing costs. Think of picking like this: as consumers, when we are searching for a specific brand or type of bread in a store, it can take us a few extra rounds along different aisles. For every product, we have to spend a few minutes walking around and searching for it. As consumers, a few extra minutes does not matter. If nothing else, every stroll past a new aisle helps us see new options in the market.

For a warehouse manager, every second counts. Especially when millions of products have to be picked. So, time is of consequence. While robots help in warehousing, AR can help workers become more productive.

Workers are given AR headsets that have the entire warehouse mapped and visible on the screen. Armed with this headset, the worker knows exactly where to go, what to pick, scan, and even how and when to assess the inventory. This sharply reduces execution time and hikes efficiency. For e-commerce companies too, AR can play a big role. By wearing headsets, the delivery team can see the exact house of the consumer. By reducing delivery time by a few minutes for each package, the on-ground team can reach more houses within a day.

This is what DHL says about its AR programme. DHL Supply Chain is rolling out the next phase of its Vision Picking Program following a successful trial of augmented reality technology in the Netherlands. Since the trial, DHL and partners Google,

Vuzix, and Ubimax have refined the vision-picking solution, and DHL is now expanding the programme across different industry sectors on a global scale, forging another step forward for AR solutions in logistics.

Its initial phase focuses on pilots in the US, the Netherlands, and the UK. The augmented reality and virtual reality market is expected to be the next big breakthrough technology, especially after the success of Pokemon Go. Gaming is a small part of the market, as AR will see applications in myriad industries, including enterprise management and training, lifestyle and healthcare, and location-based solutions. Goldman Sachs estimates a market of $80 billion for both virtual and augmented reality by 2025.[2]

The other big technology, of course, is unmanned aerial vehicles or drones. Amazon and DHL are leading the way on this front. DHL Parcel has successfully concluded a three-month test of its third Parcelcopter generation. The trial run, part of a larger research and innovation project, was conducted between January and March 2016 in the Bavarian community of Reit im Winkl. It is the first time in the world that a parcel service provider directly integrated a parcelcopter logistically into its delivery chain, says DHL.[3]

It is in the last few years that the Indian logistics industry has sped up to meet and match the best practices in the rest of the world. Fleet management is no longer about a dusty room in a garage where maps and pins depict the last-known locations of trucks and containers; instead, companies have embraced the benefits of information technology and modernized their systems, obtaining precise and real-time data on what's happening.

Hand-held scanners, once prohibitively expensive and complicated, have now been integrated with wireless networks so that workers can quickly scan the items that need to be transported. Smartphones and tablets are being used to complete the ecosystem by feeding into and reading from centralized databases, speeding up the time-to-transport and reducing errors brought about by haste or illiteracy. In fact, some warehouses use overhead displays to tell their employees what and how to pack, getting around the problem of functional illiteracies or ill-matched skillsets.

One of the biggest drivers of growth in the country has been the emergence of last-mile delivery services that promise to solve, as the name suggests, one of the most troublesome tasks for a large-scale shipper – finding a faster, easier, and cheaper way of getting their consignments into the hands of customers. One of the key innovations is typical of the *jugaad* we Indians are famous for: instead of using three- or four-wheelers for last-mile deliveries, the new-gen 3PLs now use two-wheelers that are cheaper to operate (usually, they belong to the delivery executives themselves who are given a daily allowance for petrol) and can navigate traffic faster.

Tracking technology, as elsewhere in the world, is also becoming increasingly commonplace in the country. India is no longer a decade behind the West when it comes to best practices, as used to be the case until the late 2000s. With home-grown companies like Future Retail, Aditya Birla Group's More, and others willing to invest in talent and technology, it is no wonder then that the automatic shelf-stocking systems that are instrumental in maintaining the slim margins prevalent in the highly-competitive retail industry have been adopted faithfully.

The Goods and Services Tax will finally allow logistics companies the freedom to consolidate their warehouses and set up mega-distribution centres that can service multiple states. At present, each state has its own tax regime in addition to the central government's, and this adds both complexity and costs to operations. The GST is expected to simplify the administration of taxation. Operationally, this will also mean the withdrawal of border check posts, and this will decrease the time trucks spend waiting for clearances, thereby increasing the speed of deliveries.

Indian companies are gearing up with new technologies to meet the challenges they expect to face in the coming decade. Hear what Malcolm Monteiro, CEO, Asia-Pacific, DHL e-commerce, has to say about India: 'I believe the future of logistics is paved with innovation and technology. Today, the industry is constantly piloting, testing, and adopting these technologies to provide more efficient, reliable, and sustainable delivery. This enables us to test, pilot, and adopt innovations in logistics, such as drone deliveries, robotics in warehouses, autonomous vehicles, etc.'

While logistics companies innovate, their clients have to adapt too. 'Amidst this environment of constant change, businesses need to constantly innovate to meet the demands of their customers and stay relevant. For instance, the rise of e-commerce has triggered changing consumer behaviour and expectations. Consumers expect choice, convenience, and control in their delivery when they purchase an item online. This places a lot of demands on their entire logistics chain,' Monteiro says.

'For example, in India, we saw a need for a solution to enable consumers to receive shipments 24x7 at their convenience. In response, we developed a Parcel Locker solution using mobile technology to ensure customers get all-day access to their shipments from a safe, secure, and convenient facility via a unique security code conveyed to them by SMS. We also designed Smart Trucks to solve urban logistics challenges such as traffic restriction, density, and clogging, ensuring that our customers enjoy on-time delivery. These Smart Trucks employ the use of technologies and information sources to optimize routes.

'In India, the e-commerce industry is expected to grow to US $100 billion by 2020, largely fuelled by technology-enabled innovations such as digital payments, analytics-driven customer engagement, etc. For companies in India looking to tap this opportunity, it is crucial that they continually innovate and implement relevant solutions in their business.'

DHL has announced an investment of €70 million to strengthen its operations to meet the fast-growing demand for quality e-commerce logistics services in India, and will expand its air hubs in Delhi and Mumbai.

The local investment will be through its Indian subsidiary, Blue Dart Express. Blue Dart currently operates thirteen air hubs in India as part of its network in the e-commerce logistics business. Its air hubs in Delhi and Mumbai (measuring 5,761 sq. m. and 4,274 sq. m. respectively) will be equipped with automation to handle a daily volume of over 500 tonnes. The automation in both air hubs enables Blue Dart to process higher volumes of inbound and outbound shipments in a shorter span of time for distribution to consumers across India by air.

*

Other popular technologies being applied in logistics include natural language processing bots or NLP bots. These are software applications that allow consumers or clients of a company to chat in real-time, simulating a human conversation. NLP bots have several applications, and they replace call centre executives with robotic FAQ done in a real-time fashion.

Increasing numbers of scientists are devoting their energy to logistical solutions. According to a report published in the *Economic Times*, the next generation of work is already underway in India.[4]

To deliver high-end technology in logistic solutions, the industry is hiring senior scientists previously engaged in top-end research to focus on their core requirement – the efficient delivery of goods. That involves creating algorithms for identifying where warehouses should be located, to geocoding and making last-mile delivery of products smoother.

Companies like Zomato, Delhivery, Ekart, and Locus are seeking inputs from these companies to seek even smarter ways of ensuring efficient warehouse location, management, and delivery. However, it is an undeniable truth that no company is shaking things up in this sector as much as e-commerce giant Amazon.[5]

While many of Amazon's disruptive moves in the industry can be termed business moves – such as it getting into freight itself, offering same-day, one-hour deliveries, etc., they have been accompanied by tech-driven process re-engineering as well.[6] In 2016, Amazon was reportedly using over 30,000 robots in its warehouses – robots that were rolled out by its acquired subsidiary. The acquisition itself was a masterstroke in the business world; through the purchase of Kiva Systems (now

Amazon Robotics), Amazon ensured that its technology was not made available to its competitors.[7]

In addition to Kiva/AR and GreyOrange, Fetch and Harvest are also quite prominent in this field. With necessity always proving to be the mother of invention, there is little doubt then that the automation space in logistics is still only warming up.

*

Management and tracking of assets, people, and services has emerged an important aspect of enterprise management. IoT is a network of devices that communicate among themselves using mobile connectivity to address specific functions or processes. For instance, some of the common use of IoT applications is around public utility services such as street lighting, waste management, parking management, etc. It can also be used for applications related to healthcare, education, and physical safety and security.

Fundamental to this is the machine-to-machine or M2M concept. While M2M consists of communication and data exchange within a cluster, or a defined set, of devices, IoT works on the same principle, but on a much grander scale. M2M is relevant to enterprises as well as to end users, and today almost every industry is able to take its processes to the next level with the help of this technology. It has brought about transformational changes in organizations, helping them achieve transparency in operations, access to real-time information, and a faster response time.

IoT and M2M together have great potential to transform India, and are expected to be the key enablers for Digital India

Vision, Make in India, and smart cities – missions that have been proposed in the country. Given the growth potential of the market to triple to $1.7 trillion by 2020 (IDC), IoT is, naturally, being adopted in different aspects of enterprise management. While the concept of connecting even household devices to the Internet is growing, devices, connectivity, and IT services will make up the majority of the IoT market by 2020.

M2M/IoT Signals by Airtel

Over the past few years, telecom service providers have built several unique solutions in India. These work across private sector, local government, and utility providers. India's largest telecom service provider, Airtel, has focused its attention on M2M/IoT solutions. Airtel says it has devoted substantial focus and effort in building capabilities in the M2M and IoT space. With over 2.5 million M2M end points on Airtel across the length and breadth of India, many of the country's vehicle and asset-tracking solutions, smart utility monitoring solutions, and secure banking transactions are powered by Airtel's M2M/IoT technology.

In the recent past, Airtel has added several platform capabilities to make its M2M/IoT offerings more comprehensive so as to address the emerging challenges in this evolving space. The addition of several security and SIM management features for enterprises to deploy large-scale M2M/IoT projects with minimal security threats and no potential misuse of SIM cards is one such instance. These capabilities are a mix of in-house development and technology partnerships that were developed to bring IoT solutions to the market. Airtel has deployed several real-time projects with numerous enterprise customers to not only improve their operational efficiencies but also to enhance some of their product offerings. Some of the examples where Airtel has deployed M2M/IoT are in smart metering, traffic management, and asset tracking.

Smart Metering

Smart metering (with an inbuilt SIM card) communication technology allows the electricity meter to be read from a central point. To capture the reading, the meter electronically puts into play a series of actions: collecting energy-use information, verifying its accuracy to check for pilferage, and processing it for monitoring and billing. As a part of the project, Airtel offers M2M Smart Meter solutions to eleven state electricity boards. This helps the state to reduce outages and interruptions in power, identify losses in the distribution set-up, and effectively monitor the performance of transformers and grids. The Automatic Meter Data Reading has benefited customers too, ensuring customer satisfaction for the electricity boards.

Asset Tracking Solution

Airtel has developed a unique GSM + GPS + RFID-based tracking solution which delivers several benefits to the customer. For instance, the solution has the capability to track assets even when they are indoor, and can do so by using a fraction of the power that a GPS would use. The solution is also capable of sending out alerts to a defined audience based on the rules a customer chooses to define.

For example:

- A transport aggregator is able to track shipments even when the trucks change.
- A manufacturing/mining unit is able to track the well-being of its workers, who often work in hazardous circumstances
- A school is able to provide real-time updates to parents about the exact location of their wards, as to whether they are in a library or in the playground.

Equipment Monitoring Solution

Airtel has also developed end-to-end solutions including the device, management platforms, and connectivity to help monitor the health and other critical parameters of remotely-deployed industrial/consumer equipment. The system takes critical readings from the equipment, translates it into meaningful alerts and information, and feeds it into the existing systems of the enterprise. Using these capabilities:

- A white goods manufacturer is able to predict and proactively service faults in the field, while reducing the repeat visits to half.
- A FMCG company is able to accurately measure the health of its inventory in a cold chain and take prompt actions proactively.

Traffic Management Solution

Airtel Business's traffic management solution has enabled the traffic police in several cities and regions to build real-time m-challan solutions which enable the traffic police to:

- Pull out past records of the offender in real-time, while issuing a challan.
- Monitor the availability of personnel and traffic violations at any spot in the city.
- Integrate the data with several other data bases like those of courts, RTO, etc.
- Accept digital payments if the violator has run out of cash.

The telecom connectivity that service providers like Airtel offer are now the foundation of thousands of solutions for businesses in India and across the world.

*

AI and Robotics Power Writer

Denzil De Souza is an unassuming chairman of a global company, Writer Corporation. Known for its moving, relocation, and cash-management services, Writer Corp is based in Mumbai but works across markets in South Asia and the Middle East.

Writer Corporation manages ₹3,500 crore of cash for 18,000 bank ATMs and 12,000 retail points every day, using 900 vehicles and 60 vaults. Its relocation services are equally widespread, with 15,000 moves per year for more than 3,000 clients. All this is run and done with a strong technology backbone (that allows for GPS monitoring of vans) with a 24x7 command centre and automated call centres.

Writer Corporation has an interesting history. The company was established at the 'hour' of India's independence in 1947 by P. N. Writer in Mumbai. It was a small packing company when Denzil's father Charles joined the firm. A few years later,

Charles bought the company from P. N. Writer and focused on growing it into a global corporation. Renamed Writer Corporation, the firm grew rapidly, and is now accounted among the largest move-management companies in the world.

A diversification into information management began in 1987, when Writer Corporation realized the need for secure retention and storage of critical documents. The company began by creating storage centres where client companies could store important documents in a safe but easily retrievable system. 'Though the initial effort was on physical storage, the company has grown to do online and digital storage of documents,' says De Souza. Writer Corporation is now the largest integrated information management company in India.

There is a natural logic to the move to digital that the company anticipated earlier than others. Digitization of documents became a part of the overall business process services that they undertake for their clients.

While converging and enabling communication between the physical and digital worlds is the essence of Writer's 'Industry 4.0', its digital innovation governing outcomes are referred to as 4E output – Enrich, Enhance, Enable, and Ensure.

- Enrich customer experience
- Enhance business growth
- Enable operational efficiency
- Ensure cyber protection

'Our eagerness to be game changers in the business process services market and our constant pursuit to create a wow factor for our customers, has made us design our new-age service offerings, totally leveraging digital innovation 4.0 and thereby targeting the 4E outcomes,' De Souza says.

Writer's approach was to ensure that a customized digital solution for every process outsourced to it would interface with the physical and digital worlds. 'We designed our solutions, tapping new-age technologies of artificial intelligence, robotics, and machine learning to provide a next gen experience to end customers,' De Souza says.

Its clients for business process services and information management in India include ICICI Bank, HSBC India, Axis Bank, Whirlpool India, TCS, and Airtel. Writer has built a set of technology-enabled BPO service offerings leveraging platforms like AI, social, mobile, analytics, and the cloud. This allows its customers to enhance their operations with minimal overheads and maximum reach.

Most of the demographic data and regulatory evidences worldwide are collected in physical form. While there are attempts to go digital, dependency on paper is still high, especially in third-world countries owing to their population. Further, in the age of analytics, there is no end to the quantity of information collected across processes. In such a scenario, customers in the services industry globally are still looking for assisted channels for processing rather than for self-assisted digital channels. While for a few, apps and digital channels could be the preference, there are quite a lot of tedious processes like scanning and storing documents that still need manual intervention even in the present day.

Established BPOs servicing these processes as on date operate on a model of digitized physical data form, followed by image-based data entry. Even large BPO players are unable to crack this stage of image-based data entry in the execution of this process. The problem becomes much more complex when demographic forms are hand-written or in the vernacular script. This means duplication of effort and low productivity on account of compulsive manual conversion of physical to digital data.

The most critical aspect of business, turnaround time (TAT) for transaction activation, is directly impacted by manual interventions and lack of data handshakes when individual applications are not tied together. A data processing application, even at best output speed but not passing real-time data to the core business application, is of no help in improving turnaround times.

Writer has aimed to resolve these pain points using emerging technologies, specially reinforcement learning in the AI portfolio, and usage of smart application integration.

Robotics Enabled Payment/Direct Debit Mandate Management

The Mandate Management solution of Writer Corporation is an example of its robotics-enabled automation capabilities. Using intelligent character recognition (ICR) tools, the solution has automated data extraction for the mandate form, eliminating data entry as a phase in the process execution. After the checker verification phase is done, the mandate is submitted to the National Payment gateway (NPCI) interface for mandate verification. The XML and digitized image of the form are uploaded to the NPCI server through a send service. Response XML is received by Writer's mandate management application to decipher success of the transaction.

The checker process is accelerated on account of an AI tool included in the ICR solution. Spelling corrections, location name alterations based on trends, reverse updates to the inbuilt dictionary are some smart features that the AI software has added to the solution.

The AI has allowed the company to create a database of corrections that helps in reducing future errors. Once it is linked with the bank payment process, it ensures minimal error and higher level of verification.

Fully Automated Robotics-enabled Personal Loan Underwriting Process for Large Retail Bank

Typically, in Asian Banks the volume of new customers and new accounts, both on the liabilities and assets side, is very high. The extent of penetration of the Internet, digital literacy amongst rural and semi-urban terrains, and speed of processing are some of the factors which constrain Asian industry in their management of digital and physical application forms for data collection. High volumes coupled with ever-demanding TAT owing to competition, and renewed focus on cost reduction paved the way for implementation of new-age solutions. For large private sector banks, Writer devised a robotics loan process solution that has three distinct features enabling near 100 per cent automation. As a result, all the associated benefits of cost optimization, improved TAT, and lower risk of fraudulent processing of information, are passed on to the client.

Feature 1: Physical form converted into digital data by using ICR/OCR technology. As ICR/OCR has limited success rate in the case of manual scripts, to enhance accuracy the company has introduced a 'Robotics Process engine'. The extracted data using an ICR/OCR engine passes through these automated rules; a 'robot' validates the data collected and alters values based on a pre-processed database. The database will be enriched with every correction that is made and has the ability to store and retrieve millions of patterns/combinations. Robotic process automation (RPA) is the application of technology that allows configuration of software or a 'robot' to capture and interpret existing applications for processing a transaction, manipulating data, triggering responses, and communicating with other digital systems.

Feature 2: Writer's loan processing solution has been created with the flexibility of capturing KYC information from multiple document types, namely the passport, PAN card, Aadhaar card, and utility bills as well as the digitized copy of the KYC document. The data capture phase acts as the initial inwarding phase of an enrolment process and integrates with a decision engine. The decision engine has been built using analytical models to derive inferences from the data captured and cross-checks the veracity of the data read by the application automatically. Checks and balances ensure there is an additional layer of data validation.

Feature 3: This processed data helps underwrite the credit score and then passes the transaction to the core business application for credit decision. Credit decision involves a delegation of powers and hence is to be routed to different stakeholders for approval. To facilitate auto-routing of the proposals, a work-flow tool was integrated with the decision engine. This made the Writer solution fully integrated and automated.

The other highlight of the Writer loan process solution is that this can work in a 'tab-based' data capture model for single-case handling as well as in a server model for bulk processes across thousands of records using the robotics solution.

IoT-Driven Solar Panel Solution for Records Warehouse

Another smart technology innovation at Writer's is the implementation of an IoT-driven solar panel solution for records management warehouses in India. While the facility uses solar-driven power for 85 per cent of its requirements, the solution is an IP-driven device-configuration that provides statistics around consumption and performance. Reports are auto-emailed to the admin team, which checks for below-benchmark numbers to manage corrective actions. An IoT solution like this one is effective in that it enables logical data collection between physical devices embedded for a common function.

These dashboards are received at the central monitoring hub of the solar panel solution provider that records, analyses, and ploughs back device improvements and efficiencies to the process. Apart from reporting automation and a technology-integrated solution, it has provided synergies in manpower utilization on the engagement. No support team is required on the ground; nor are site supervisors expected to visit the facility for performance measurement, data collection, and analysis.

A logical next step to the solution is to leverage learnings from the efficiencies of the solar panel implementation across facilities in different geographies. The reports analysed at a common hub can help performance-comparison and benchmark creation using sufficient data gathered from across the company's pan-India facilities. Cost savings and a direct positive impact to the company's business margins only helps offer better services to records management customers.

With the changes in India arising from implementation of GST, warehousing, data management, robotics, and analytics will be key factors ensuring efficiency and profitability. In many ways, the benefits of GST and a single-tax market will be delivered through high-tech logistics solutions. In some ways, this is one sector where the tax policy is in tandem with the industry.

4

CONSUMER AND RETAIL

Philips Light Network

Harsh Chitale begins to glow when you ask him about light and sensors. His excitement about lighting is infectious enough to illuminate the room he occupies. As the vice-chairman and MD of Philips Lighting India, the IIT-educated electrical engineer is pioneering the use of lighting in more ways than one can imagine. Philips now promotes its products with the tagline 'Lighting beyond illumination'.

Chitale is living this philosophy. 'Light is not just light any more. Light acts as a sensor of temperature, light acts as a sensor of a person, light acts as a position locator, light is able to communicate, and light has embedded intelligence,' he says. These are the new applications of lighting – smart, connected and sensor-enabled – that are changing the way we use light bulbs in homes, offices, factories, shops, and almost everywhere.

Earlier, a light bulb was just a light bulb. Now a light bulb embedded in a sensor-based system can track, trace, and send information about the ambient area to a connected server.

This has many uses. From mapping the number of people in a room to minimizing use of electricity, to tracking objects in a warehouse, light is being used by some *avant garde* companies as an important employee-engagement tool.

As India's business landscape matures, employee productivity and overall employee well-being are becoming critical for every organization. It is fast becoming the norm to map the expectations of the new generation of employees. Some forward-thinking businesses are beginning to realize that to gain a competitive edge among a growing pool of international employers and to attract and retain top talent, employees must be given the right environment to thrive and to flourish in.

Nowhere is this more evident than in India's hi-tech sector, where the importance of recruiting and nurturing the brightest employees is mission-critical. Increasingly, we see employers adopting new technologies that allow them to harness the best from their teams and, in turn, boost their engagement and productivity.

Recognizing the importance of this approach, enterprises like Intel are leading the way in using connected LED lighting systems that can create smart, secure, and interactive offices of the future. For example, the staff at Intel's new Bengaluru research campus will soon use their smartphones to control aspects of their work environment such as lighting and air-conditioning, thanks to IoT technology from Philips Lighting and Cisco.

Lighting is everywhere, in streets, public spaces, offices, and homes. In 2006, there were approximately 43.8 billion light points globally – estimates predict that by 2030 there will be 59.2 billion light points globally, a 35 per cent increase.[1] If we consider public lighting alone, there are approximately 300 million street lights worldwide. It would be financially foolish to overlook a physical infrastructure that is already in place.

Additionally, cities have to become more energy efficient – for the planet, as well as for their own budgets. Currently, 15 per cent of the world's energy demand is for lighting. A global transition to LED technology will bring energy savings of 53 per cent by 2030, but when LED lights are connected and controlled wirelessly via IoT, energy savings can increase by as much as 80 per cent compared with use of incandescent technologies.

The sensors embedded in the LED lighting fixtures – that are themselves connected and powered by the office IT network – enable lighting systems to become pathways of information, delivering updates on everything from room occupancy to temperature and humidity. In the case of Intel, 10,000 connected LED luminaires are being installed throughout the state-of-the-art facility, 5,000 of which are equipped with sensors and are on the Powered over Ethernet (PoE) network. This means building managers can monitor and analyse building usage data in real-time and identify efficiencies that extend much beyond just energy savings.

Connected LED lighting can drive down energy consumption by up to 80 per cent compared with conventional lighting, allowing businesses to slash their carbon footprint and drastically reduce their running costs. In the near future, we will see LED lighting integrated into different surfaces, for example carpets, that can help staff and visitors navigate offices, displaying directions and ensuring safety.

Already we can see light-points acting as an 'in-premise' GPS to get the exact location of an individual inside a building or a mall, providing contextual, personalized information to that individual. In the office setting, this could mean helping staff members find availability of nearby meeting rooms, helping them improve productivity.

'In God we trust. Everyone else must bring data.'

There are few words that are as holy writ to a good manager as Edward Deming's most famous phrase. The quest for data – better data, better being a function of precision, depth, and timeliness – has for a long time been an objective as important as anything else in every industry operating in the world today. Whether it's a successful company or a struggling one, whether it's customer profiling or competition assessment, demand forecasting or root cause analyses, companies live and die on the sword of data. The world might romanticize entrepreneurs like Branson and Buffet who swear by their gut instincts, but all said and done, there aren't many businessmen today (especially among the captains of their industries) who can afford to act in the face of contrasting data or in the absence of supporting information. Even the most trusted CEO has a board he must answer to if an instinct not backed by 'proof' fails to pay off.

Until commercial computing really took off, most companies had to rely on their personnel to understand their customers' preferences. The 'data', as it was supplied then, was mostly subjective, and taken at face value mostly because it could not be disputed indisputably. As a result, business decisions up and down the chain were subject to the vagaries of human perception at each and every important level. If the production side was better, in that its in-house nature afforded it a more reliable source of data, the consumption side was anybody's guess.

But the introduction of computers, and more importantly, data banks that could store hundreds of thousands of transactions, altered the landscape for consumer industries. Companies no longer relied on 'felt' data because they could run sophisticated (for the time) programs that would aggregate numbers that could help identify issues, trends, and hypotheses.

One of the first computers developed for a business concern, the LEO (Lyons Electric Office I), would be rudimentary by today's standards, but it was a visionary step at the time of its launch in 1951. A few years later, mainframes would become the in-thing, a must-have for every business serious about its work. Batch processes were used to process tons of data points before spouting out numbers that the managers tried to translate into real-world equivalents.

But the data processing rate was slow, and insights not immediate. Any requests to process data would involve a queue, a priority system.

Then the Internet arrived, and with that the networked corporation. Even far-flung 'outposts' became an integral part of the company, feeding in real-time data and enabling granular-level assessment of the same. Processing became more democratic; servers stored data and could handle thousands of requests at the same time, but you still required a human hand pecking away at a keyboard to ask the right questions. The computing power was distributed, with servers handling some of the load while local workstations handled the rest (spreadsheets).

Paradigm shift again. In the last decade and a half, it is no longer enough for machines to present us with the data that we need to reach a conclusion. Developments in AI and ML mean that the human hand may soon be redundant when it comes to asking the right question itself. The computers are being trained to look for patterns and learn, much as a human being does, what to do on encountering a pattern or two.

AI has come of age in recent years, particularly because of the efforts now being directed towards goal- or environment-specific AI systems instead of the over-hyped AI-can-do-anything solutions sought in the 1960s and 1980s. With man understanding his own thought processes better and becoming more adept at translating that rubric into something a machine can follow, the capabilities of an artificially-intelligent machine is now several fold what it was even half a decade ago.

There are now computers that can track video feeds and pick out faces based on points of identification; there are systems that monitor footfalls in retail outlets (banks, supermarkets, etc.) and determine the probable routes of a customer so that (advertising) communication is both optimal and subtle. (e.g. Beacon). This means that even sales personnel can be moved around like pieces on a chessboard so that they build on a unified approach to the customer instead of talking at cross-purposes or even losing the customer. These are all examples of highly specific AI machines.

Keeping track of customers also helps to lower turnaround times. Re-targeting, which is why you see ads for a mobile phone on a non-commercial website shortly after you checked out what an e-com site had to offer on mobile phones, is a happening trend that e-coms hope will bring down their bounce rates and bounce up their click-throughs.

Fewer inputs from customers typically result in greater customer satisfaction, but fewer inputs also imply less data. So, unification of databases, and correlating information such as personal details, history, events, and triggers will help give a complete picture of the customer to a company without losing his goodwill or even making it appear as if the company is getting too much information about him.

Social media research was a brief phenomenon because it allowed companies access to quality, specific, and actionable feedback instead of generalized, reduced feedback. Many of these companies, especially with human resources, who had a similar background, eventually turned into data miners, placing as much reliance on machine-learned data interpretation as on human-based gleanings.

Smart Public Lighting

Philips partnered with Naya Raipur Development Authority (NRDA), providing energy-efficient LED street lights and lighting control systems for the newly planned city. NRDA planned to develop Raipur as a 'green and smart city' in every sense. They were looking for energy-efficient lighting solutions for lighting up many roads in the city.

Philips used its AmpLight Systems, which is a group-level control system for outdoor street lights. Up to fifty street lights can be controlled using one AmpLight system through a cabinet. With AmpLight controls, one can remotely monitor the performance of street lights leading to more efficient operations. This also makes the entire switching on/off of the street lights very efficient, wherein a simple message can be sent by the person managing the street to switch the lights on/off. This is just one basic functionality of the AmpLight system.

The AmpLight solution is a complete web-based solution with advanced communication and easy integration with existing installations. A centralized solution is easy to implement and requires less equipment and easier installation than a pole-based standalone solution. AmpLight is a solution that combines cost saving and lower emissions without compromising on quality and safety.

In the case of NRDA, the complete hosting and connectivity solution was also provided by Philips Lighting.

In addition to this project, Philips Lighting has also recently won one of the first orders for Smart Connected Lighting for a Smart City Project in western India which will use more than 5,000 AmpLight Systems to control 70,000 Smart Street Light Points. This is one of the largest managed services order for street lights globally, says Philips.

Smart Warehouse Lighting

In the past, conventional lighting technology and lack of lighting controls meant that lighting had to be permanently on to ensure safety. In 24x7 operations such as warehouses, this was costly to run and not sustainable financially.

Warehouse lighting today is not about just illumination. With the right lighting, the mood in the warehouse improves. Energy levels rise. And when workers feel energized and comfortable, productivity flows.

Additionally, there are environmental benefits too. Presence-detectors ensure spaces are only fully lit when needed. Which means lower carbon emissions and lower energy bills.

A warehouse isn't one giant building. It's a series of individual spaces serving different functions such as loading bays, racking areas, etc. These spaces require different kinds of lighting and are often in use at different times. Lighting a complete warehouse round the clock wastes energy, and runs up unnecessary and huge power bills.

Philips Lighting has implemented complete Smart Warehouse Lighting for one of the major e-commerce players in India. Philips Lighting has used a complete wired control lighting network, with its Dynalite Systems that delivers high-quality light only when and where it's needed. With the use of this Smart Lighting, the warehouse can be divided into 'zones' or areas. Presence detectors, placed throughout each of the areas, trigger full-output lighting when movement is detected in, or is approaching, a 'zone', ensuring people and vehicles can move around the warehouse safely. When a space is unoccupied, lighting dims to an energy-saving lower level – an ambient light. This zoning and right scheduling ensures that the warehouse operates efficiently, leading to operational savings much beyond just simple energy savings.

Smart Warehouse Lighting lets you illuminate specific areas in a single space by creating lighting zones. The zones 'group' luminaires together, so they brighten and dim as one unit.

Configuring zones is really easy – it is done via remote control. You can create the zones to suit the layout of your warehouse, then set the lighting levels for when a space is occupied and the background lighting level for when it's unoccupied.

Smart Warehouse Lighting gives a lot of flexibility to users. If the organization wants to change the warehouse layout the zones can be just re-configured with the remote.

*

Artie, Myntra's Fashion Designer

Like Philips lighting, there are several consumer products and services companies that are deploying technologies for solutions that weren't even imagined before. E-commerce has now become part of the Indian middle-class vocabulary, and the technology being used in e-commerce is surprisingly inventive.

Consumer goods e-commerce player Myntra has created Moda Rapido, a line of fashion garments where the chief designer is an artificial intelligence robot called Artie. In a world where fashions and styles are changing constantly, marketers need help on the go. Artie trawls the net for the latest trends in t-shirts, jeans, shirts, kurtas, shoes, tops, etc. The robot then puts together several options for several products and offers it to the product team of Myntra. The team then tailors the suggestions to the market and releases the styles for consumers.

Artie is involved in product design, production planning, manufacturing, and demand forecasting. Myntra has become the first e-commerce company in India to use AI for commercial products. In the last few years, the Moda Rapido brand has become one of its bestselling ranges. Artie also helps in analysing the sales data and offering feedback to the product managers.

Artie can design up to 100 t-shirts a day while a human designer takes about two days for a single t-shirt. The typical fashion cycle is about eight months, from concept to market. But with Artie, Myntra can get more options to the market within shorter time cycles. While earlier it was about 200 days, the time cycle for a new product has now been reduced to twenty days. This allows Moda Rapido to constantly offer new options to consumers who are keen to explore fresh designs and don't want to repeat an old look. Among young consumers, designs can get obsolete within weeks. Here the speed of an AI approach helps Myntra keep pace with the demand.

Easy Check-ins by SpiceJet

Consider another interesting use of technology by SpiceJet airline. For passengers, the most cumbersome process is checking in. Even for airlines, much of the cost of ground services includes organizing quick and convenient check-in for hundreds of passengers every hour.

The process for check-in is complicated, time consuming, people-intensive, and paper-focused. Even the self-check-in kiosks placed at many airports are not enough. Alternate queues form in front of the kiosks as many passengers take a lot of time to navigate the display and print their boarding passes. Some global airlines even request passengers to print their own baggage tags.

For Indian flyers, SpiceJet is now deploying near-field communications technology for passenger check-ins. To begin with, passengers have to download the SpiceJet app on their phones. When they enter the airport terminal they open their app and move to the posters set up by the airline.

The most interesting feature about this application is that the customer does not require to carry the itinerary printouts nor has to key in the PNR number to initiate check-in.

Near Field Communication (NFC) enables passengers to receive their boarding pass on their smart-phone when they check in through NFC-enabled smartphones with the SpiceJet mobile application. Customers who have booked their tickets using the SpiceJet mobile app will have to simply open the app and touch the mobile device on the NFC check-in poster available at the airport to get their mobile boarding pass on their smartphones.

Customers can also avail of a touch-less beacon-based check-in service to receive their boarding pass on the smartphone. Customers who have booked their tickets through the SpiceJet app will receive an alert as they walk towards the SpiceJet check-in area if their Bluetooth and the SpiceJet mobile app are on. Post acknowledgement to the notification, the customer immediately receives the boarding pass on his or her smartphone.

NFC enables short-range communication between compatible devices, whereas Beacons (Bluetooth low energy) transmits low-power signals to nearby Bluetooth-enabled mobile devices, including smartphones. Beacons broadcast short-range signals that can be detected by mobile applications on mobile devices in proximity.

The SpiceJet service has been initially introduced in Hyderabad and will soon be available in all airports supporting the e-boarding facility. This facility is set to relieve customers from standing in long queues, further enhancing their travel experience and offering them a smoother journey.

Online Listening Drives Autumn

Anusha Shetty set up Autumn Worldwide in 2010 as a marketing agency for 'social media listening'. This was an alien concept then, and even now is yet to realize its impact. While there are countless digital advertising and marketing companies, few go beyond online campaigns.

Autumn has begun deploying data analytics to capture consumer views, perceptions, and behaviour from online conversations. And it has been able to aggregate the data in a way that can offer actionable insights for marketers.

Says Shetty, 'We are in the very beginning of a revolution that is sensitive towards human actions in the digital world.' The amount of data that is being created online is growing every day. The data is in the form of text, photos, videos, and even action. No matter how advanced the world gets and moves towards automation and NLPs, there still exists the need for human intervention to harness learnings from human behaviour. The greater the creation of human data, the richer the insights; and the lag between data and insight will always have a volume-based correlation. 'The different sources that we have in Facebook and Twitter tell completely different stories with different contexts. The challenge here is to use this diverse data and bring insights that can help brands leverage them,' Shetty says.

Autumn, being at the brink of this revolution, is able to provide insights into various businesses across industries through social listening and analytics. With this expertise, businesses like Burger King and PepsiCo are at the peak of harnessing the power of data.

One of the key offerings of Autumn is Social Listening. It is the process of tracking conversations across social media platforms using relevant keywords. 'Listening' is not just about picking up @mentions or #tags; listening goes beyond just monitoring. Listening requires a mix of analysis, reflection, and the ability to narrow down on near-exact conclusions based on the data available. All these put together can point to patterns and sentiments and present real-time data to brands.

Currently, there are millions of tweets and posts a day that go out on various platforms. Data suggests that a lot of conversation is happening around categories, brands, and individuals without tagging them officially. This means there are conversations happening about 'you' or about your category (example, about MRF, the brand, and about tyre, the category) all over the Internet with some expectation of being heard. The conversations/posts can have a lot to say directly: as a message, sentiment, complaint, flaunt, expression of love, etc.; and indirectly: in its demography, psychograph, time, gender, preference, etc. Listening helps the brand track these parameters, to reflect on and use them to leverage conclusions that eventually help the brand to customize its outreach to the relevant audience through product innovations, understanding a gap in the market, and many other actionable insights.

As an industry that is growing, advertisers are constantly faced with challenges that might not have a ready solution.

Autumn uses the limited tools available in the market and guided human interventions to go through data, many times inventing tools, methods, and programs/codes specific to the requirements. This combination of effort helps deliver results and, in the process, also discover new opportunities. The following examples illustrate this:

PepsiCo – Quaker Oats

Currently, food habits are changing in parallel with a strong trend towards becoming or continuing to stay fit. One of PepsiCo's nutrition brands is Quaker Oats. The company was determined to see how nutritionally conscious people are about their breakfast in this day of the fast-changing fitness frenzied lifestyle. Breakfast in the urban context has slowly dwindled to quick fixes with expectations of quick results. However, there is a perception that healthy food is bland or tasteless and that one needs to compromise on taste to achieve the end goal of a healthy body. The objective before Autumn was to try to understand what a healthy breakfast means to the audience. To arrive at the answer, Autumn could have exercised the option of using multiple methods, including personal interviews or questionnaires. But these methods are time-consuming and need high resources without any significant guarantee of accuracy. Sometimes even the audience size is questioned. With its tools, Autumn was able to capture real-time sentiments, opinions, and viewpoints – the ideally representative data-set, in other words. This is the data that will help the client arrive at answers and conclusions.

Using Twitter Advanced Search and Google Keyword Planner, Autumn can identify the relevant keywords and phrases that people use to converse on a topic; these are, in turn, cross-checked against the river of news on the social-listening tool. It collected earned data from Twitter, Facebook, forums, and mainstream media conversations using the same tool.

The next step is to consolidate the data for better integrity. Wordle, Tagul, Word Frequency Counter, and Excel Macros were used to identify and remove spam words.

This is a perfect example of how available tools, along with invented tools and human intervention, come together to provide a solution. The social-listening tool helped Autumn fetch conversations, macros helped fetch demographics, and a bit of manual work connected professions and respondents.

This work received recognition from PepsiCo for 'The Most Forward-looking Insights Work Done', despite Autumn not being a conventional research agency.

Burger King

Consumers of fast food primarily look for Value For Money (VFM), taste, and quality, possibly in that very order. Along with this, consumers also seek an overall brand experience; hence the need for the consistency of this experience, affordability, and, you guessed it, speed and ease of ordering.

When we talk about speed, we need to also remember that social media is now considered to be faster than complaint centres and customer service teams. Even though a complaint may be re-routed to the complaint cell, the consumer is always under the impression that social media helped him/her achieve a faster resolution than would have been the case otherwise. Similarly, brands are keenly aware too that one negative comment can escalate within no time and more people than one would like would hear about the brand negatively.

As part of its process, Autumn uses relevant keywords and fetches data from Twitter, Instagram, Facebook, and Zomato, some via tools and some via human interventions. This data is then analysed through guided manual interventions and segregated into brand factors like imagery, product, loyalty, service, infrastructure, health, and price. These categories help the companies to see exactly how the consumer feels about its brand and its products.

This is where Online Reputation Management (ORM) comes in; the process of improving the brand's imagery online along with adding positive material to increase trust in the brand. This is not just countering or resolving negative commentary about the brand, but also talking to consumers who love Burger King, for instance. Autumn becomes the voice of the brand, and in turn the consumer feels he has been heard. This way Autumn strengthens the online credibility of brands by being approachable and always dependable.

The analysis of data helps bring in the insights. This is done with a combination of human interventions, the social-listening tool, Macros, and R Statistics. Once Autumn has categorized the data, it can tell what the consumer sentiments are. It can identify positive influencers for the brand, products that have delighted the consumers, and staff behaviour at the stores, among other details. These are the details that help Burger King improve its services and take feedback, positive or negative, to navigate through the ever-changing world of fast food and social media, according to the Autumn team.

In one case, Autumn engaged with actor Priyanka Chopra to understand her preferences. With its listening exercise, Autumn learnt she was a fan of the Burger King brand. This information was then leveraged to create a conversation with her on Twitter, in turn fetching multiple eye balls for the brand.

Apart from this, Autumn is able to predict patterns and habits of its clients' consumers, so that the clients can customize their approach to consumers, allowing for maximum conversions. The client in each case is able to grasp data that is readily available to provide the most relevant conclusions.

The client is updated by data in the form of daily newsletters, weekly ORM reports, monthly audits, and yearly reviews. Here, Macros are used to consolidate the data, along with human intervention. The daily newsletter is merely a way for the client to stay up-to-date on daily commentary about the brand. The ORM report is a good way to look back on the week's happenings and confirm if the company addressed all queries that came its way. The monthly reports are presented along with the competition's performance over the month.

Burger King as a client is confident that the brand is getting monitored live so that it is able to make quicker decisions to satisfy a customer at all points.

As an example, Burger King once flew down a fan to Mumbai from Assam on #WorldWishDay to 'delight him' as there were no stores of the brand in his city, and only because the company learnt of his love for the brand through social media.

Along with this, every store and its ambience is monitored, and ranked very often. The learnings are immense and rich. The company is able to point to exact learnings on which food or combo is a favourite with whom and why. The category itself is closely monitored, thus yielding more information on the habits and preferences of the desired audience.

The Autumn team feels that clients are now able to make smooth and confident decisions with the data available to them. For the clients, the learning is constant and not a quarterly exercise.

Burger King is using the feedback to make changes to its food items and menu composition. A few new burgers have been added as a result of the feedback from social media data analysis.

*

i2e1 Mixes ML with Drinks

Tracking consumer behaviour can be done in other ways too, such as through free Wi-Fi connections. While the consumer is happy to get a free service, the commercial entity earns valuable information. The simple act of sipping tea at a café is infused with machine learning.

The country consumes 8,37,000 tonnes of tea every year. A bunch of IIT–IIM graduates working out of a 150 sq. ft. office space is bringing a little bit of ML in your next cup of chai.

For i2e1 (Information to Every One), an IIT Delhi-based start-up, the model is simple enough – locate café owners, including some of the top chains as well as small tea sellers, and provide free Wi-Fi to the end user using a cloud-based management layer created by i2e1. The end user is allocated data limits, which is dynamically allocated based on the user profile. Users have to provide basic information about themselves, like their phone number, while accessing the Wi-Fi.

Since free Wi-Fi requires the end user to log in, the service provider can track the online activities of the consumer and use the information accordingly. Wi-Fi usage across multiple properties, coupled with millions of other data points, such as beacons, third party APIs, and sales data become the raw material for creating individualized preferences – for beverages, with sugar or sugar free, types of food items, etc. – for each user. The AI-based algorithms created by i2e1 then converts them into insights and actionable information.

Starting from decisions to setting up the next shop to managing outdoor traffic real-time at multiple such outlets, the use cases are multiple. User preferences and repeat behaviour across thousands of such outlets help location owners understand their customers much better. These insights are converted into individualized offerings and i2e1's predictive algorithms ensures that you get your best cup of tea next time when you visit. Other than the tea industry, i2e1 is also helping many other brands predict the response of consumers to a new product launch.

i2e1 is also creating an offline intelligence platform powered by Wi-Fi usage for multiple segments like vehicles, hotels, garment retail, and many more. Every month, more than 100TB of data is structured, analysed, and converted into meaningful insights. End-users get easy and affordable access to the Internet, while brands and merchants get increased business. The intelligence helps companies provide relevant and timely product offerings to customers. It is not only the right type but the right time that the platform focuses on. Multiple clients have benefited from a cost reduction of 15 per cent and a response increase of 26 per cent, which means more revenue from end users.

The dichotomy of India is reflected in the contradiction of a country having 900 million people without Internet access while still being one of the fastest growing consumer business markets globally. Models like i2e1, which are built in India and are meant to solve issues specific to India, are bringing in real change. i2e1 is building a first-of-its-kind shareable information platform called ONE. In the next few years, ONE aims to become an accurate intelligence platform about offline shoppers and retail locations, aiming to become the default operating system for offline analytics. It is among the first in the market to develop and deploy a 'probability to purchase score'. Unlike any other analytics company, it owns the profile data and customer identities as all its clients share their data. The company claims to cover 20 per cent of shoppers in Delhi. If Google owns online analytics, i2e1 wants to own offline analytics. Its service includes a cloud-controlled device and corresponding back-end infrastructure, which can manage Internet or Wi-Fi at an affordable price point. The device also collects locational information about non-connected smartphone users as they walk into a store or its vicinity.

The company has already developed strong traction by deploying hotspots in thousands of locations across different categories – merchants, hotels, vehicles, long stay/PGs, and small offices at as low as ₹1,000 per location. The company says its solution is being used by marquee clients such as Chai Point, The Beer Café, Ola Shuttle, NestAway, Airtel, and Vodafone, as well as by numerous other small businesses across the country. With more than 13 million device profiles, and 1 million sessions per month, i2e1 has created a cutting-edge data platform to track customer insights both online and offline.

Their 3,000-plus paying customers see significant value in its platform.

Here's how it works. When a merchant signs up with i2e1, he gets access not just to hardware, but also to a Wi-Fi management and automated CRM tool (called PRIME). PRIME is an entry point to a merchant location, using which i2e1 starts to create ONE, the integrated data platform, enabling users to carry their profiles across all its Wi-Fi hotspots. End users get affordable/free Internet and the merchants get real-time intelligence on customer profile, location dynamics, and industry trends.

In other words, the platform can seamlessly track users and their behaviour at merchant touch-points. Each time a consumer logs on to the free Wi-Fi, he or she has to create a profile. This profile is saved on the platform, and repeat activity is tracked across different merchants. The ML algorithm then predicts who will spend what based on their activity.

Leveraging this mountain of data enables i2e1 to create a ground-breaking *customer behaviour index*, where each customer is given a 'probability of purchase score'. This score can be used by a wide range of businesses – loyalty apps, payment providers, financial services firms, and of course the merchant itself – to make a customized real-time offer to the user. Its core promise to clients is, 'We make their customers "buy or buy more" every time they interact with them.'

The platform not only allows brands/merchants to reach out to customers on the premises but even after they have left the location and are using their mobile or home Internet. i2e1, thus, aims to become the 'Operating System for offline analytics' in the next five years.

It is understood that Facebook's Express Wi-Fi might operate on a similar model – providing small entrepreneurs with Wi-Fi infrastructure in (mostly) rural or under-penetrated areas in an effort to bring more users to its platform.

*

The Neuroscience of Nielsen

Understanding the mind of consumers is still a puzzle for marketers and sellers globally. There are debates as to whether companies should inculcate habit or loyalty among consumers. In the long run, do consumers buy more out of habit or loyalty? Few definitive answers can be obtained, but increasingly sophisticated tools are being used by companies to sell products and understand buying patterns.

Global information, data, and measurement company Nielsen is pioneering the use of neuroscience in India. Nielsen is investing and tapping into neuroscience to measure the sub-conscious responses of consumers to various inducements and stimuli.

Moumita Ghoshal and Janet Nair of Nielsen India provided me with a fascinating glimpse of their work in India.

Television commercials continue to consistently rank among the most preferred modes of advertising among respondents in India. While numerous studies show that many purchases are driven by emotion, most of the prevalent measurement solutions fail to capture whether an ad creates an emotional connection with viewers. Consumer neuroscience helps measure the impact of emotional advertising by assessing metrics like emotional engagement and memory activation.

Today consumers access content across myriad media, but consumers in India continue to view television commercials as among the most trustworthy means of advertising. Given the prevalence of TV in consumers' lives, however, viewers are bombarded with more ads than ever before, making it that much more difficult for brands and agencies to create commercials that truly connect with their audiences. So, what's involved in building that connection?

The media industry has a long history of measurement solutions that assess an ad's impact on its intended audience, to understand what works and what does not. But they don't determine whether an ad creates an emotional connection with the viewer. This represents a significant opportunity for marketers, because studies show that purchase decisions are emotionally driven.

Measuring Emotions

Emotions are intangible, and measuring them is no small task. Direct response surveys can be misleading because they presume that respondents can accurately verbalize their emotions. Verbal responses require respondents to express, and therefore rationalize, the emotions as feelings. Emotions are instinctive reactions to external stimuli, whereas feelings are the mind's interpretation of those emotions, and are subject to personal bias, culture, setting, past experiences, and ingrained beliefs. Moreover, many emotions don't break the surface of conscious awareness, making it impossible for them to be interpreted as feelings.

For many modern researchers, using techniques that can directly measure neurological and biological reactions is the best way to evaluate emotions. These reactions can include heart rate, sweating, posture, facial reactions, electrical impulses in specific regions of the brain, etc. Those techniques are collectively referred to as neuroscience, and recent technical innovations in this field are helping break new ground in our understanding of consumer behaviour. They are also setting a new standard for ad testing.

Neuroscience provides a deep, clear view into the real-time reactions of consumers at the most elemental level – their brainwaves. The human brain reacts to stimuli in milliseconds, and by capturing these reactions deep within the subconscious, consumer neuroscience can reveal exactly how consumers perceive brands, their marketing, and the message, at the most granular level. Pure, instantaneous, unfiltered responses measured at the subconscious level of the mind offer far more accurate and reliable insights than other consumer research methodologies.

'The metrics are obtained by measuring the brain impulses of respondents to the stimulus that is being tested,' says Ghoshal. The complete set of cutting-edge neuroscience technologies include electroencephalography (EEG) which uses sensors to collect multiple data points every second, facial coding to track emotional expressions while the consumer experiences the stimuli, biometrics to measure the emotional journey through skin conductance and heart rate, and eye-tracking to identify hot zones that the consumer focuses his gaze on and its path of navigation. While EEG provides detailed second-by-second diagnostics on the effectiveness of the stimulus, biometrics provides diagnostics on the depth of engagement; and facial coding reveals the depth of expressed emotion. This entire suite of tools guides optimization and compression of user reaction by capturing neurological and physiological response during each second of the stimulus.

While each of these measures predicts sales to some degree (EEG being the most predictive of them all), a combination of all these neuroscientific measures provides the highest level of prediction – of almost 77 per cent accuracy. While articulation in itself is much weaker in terms of predictability, when integrated with the combination of neuroscience tools it enhances the predictability to almost 84 per cent.

Consumer neuroscience measures two sets of neuro-metrics:

1. Primary metrics, resulting from real-time activity in the brain. These metrics are –

   Attention: It is a measure of how much brain energy one has to devote to the stimulus to decipher what is being shown to one.

   Emotional engagement: This indicates the extent to which the respondent is 'drawn' to the stimulus. It is the assessment of whether one is approaching or avoiding what one is seeing, and is by far the purest measure of how connected one feels with the stimulus.

   Memory Activation: This metric indicates the extent to which new memory connections get formed (encoding) or past memories are aroused (retrieval).

2. Secondary metrics, resulting from the interplay between two or more primary metrics, which are –

   Overall effectiveness: It indicates the holistic appeal that the stimulus is able to generate.

Action intent: This is the likelihood of a change in behaviour or intent to act on a message.
Comprehension: This indicates the extent to which the experience is understood or the extent to which it makes sense.
Novelty: It is the likelihood of the ad standing out and being embedded in the memory.

Vodafone

The predictive ability of neuroscience isn't restricted to the FMCG category alone. Savvy marketers handling brands like Vodafone in the telecom category also use the principles of neuroscience to engage with consumers powerfully. A recent ad under the Vodafone SuperNet™ campaign, Vodafone Super Dad, delivered a healthy performance on all the critical neuro-metrics, including overall effectiveness, action intent, and emotional engagement. The brand used various technologies to assess and deliver a superior experience to its vast spread of customers across the country.

The brand received positive audience feedback beyond the company's internal expectations. Neuroscience-based research also showed that the appeal and engagement levels were heightened further whenever the brand was referenced in the ad, indicating a positive association with the ad.

The study demonstrated that it wasn't just one segment of Vodafone's ad, but the positive contribution of most segments that led to its good performance. The ad not only benefited from a really strong start, priming the audience positively for the rest of their viewing experience, but it was also able to keep the audience engaged through most of its critical segments. That enabled effective registration of the message.

In this particular case, Vodafone had used EEG and eye-tracking to obtain the metrics.

The data collection is done either at the Nielsen Neuro Lab in Mumbai, or at remote central location venues that comply with Vodafone's neurological protocols. Nielsen says the studies are conducted individually on the subjects. Each individual goes through the entire process independently, which also ensures there is no contamination of perception that could happen in a focus group exercise.

Evidence shows that the actions and decisions of the majority of people are driven by non-conscious processes. Neuroscience helps to understand responses that people are unable, or unwilling, to articulate. Measuring non-conscious responses ensures data is without any observational, emotional or familiarity bias. With the technology now available, one can measure non-conscious responses – something traditional research misses – for a more complete view of consumers.

The frequency of this testing depends on the study objective and the client's needs. Most clients use the technology for pre-testing, for fine-tuning the commercials to their final version, for creating effective edits, and for answering other strategic questions concerning their communication.

Research algorithms are able to automatically extract compressed versions of the ad based on neurological optimality. This helps them achieve the desired output: to create the same bang but at a lesser cost. Validations have shown that 95 per cent of scientifically-compressed ads perform as well, or even better, than the originals.

This granular, second-by-second deep-dive into the ad equips advertisers with specific, immensely actionable insights. Consequently, understanding which portions of the ad to remove and which to retain for effective shorter edits becomes much more profitable for the brand.

With such strong and predictive analysis, neuroscience measures are clearly the way forward today for copy-testing applications across categories.

*

Drones Buzz at Indus Towers

Telecom companies provide services and solutions to the entire industry. But even they are equally eager to adopt new processes for their own efficiency.

Indus Towers is an interesting example of this.

Indus towers, India's largest telecom tower company, operates and manages nearly 1,20,000 towers that were built over a period of more than fifteen years. These sites comprise antenna mounting structures (like towers, monopoles, and poles), equipment housing enclosures (like shelter, cage, and shed), diesel-generator sets, air-conditioning/cooling units, outdoor equipment, external cable trays, and electrical transformers.

Cell towers are the backbone of the country's digitization drive and are important elements in the network that need to be periodically maintained for providing seamless services to customers. The health of the cell tower structure always needs to be kept in good and safe condition. This calls for periodic visual health check-ups and inspection of the complete tower structure from top to bottom. The structure has to be climbed manually for capturing the condition of every structural member – the nuts and bolts, the antenna, and the cables and equipment installed on it. This is time consuming and poses safety concerns at times to the climbing crew. There are chances of error too in manual interventions.

Indus has explored use of the evolving drone technology for bringing efficiency, safety, security, and scalability to the conventional method of cell tower inspection. With 'Drone-assisted Arial Asset Monitoring Services', complete structural inspection can be conducted without manual intervention on a typical 40-metre tower in a much safer and efficient way, and in just fifteen to twenty minutes.

These GPS-equipped drones are operated by trained pilots standing near the cell tower with remote controls. A flight path around the structure is defined, and the drone loaded with a high-resolution camera moves around the structure on this pre-defined path to capture the complete details of the towers in the form of multiple single-frame high-resolution photographs and videos.

With the help of advanced image-stitching, correction, and blending software, within a few seconds the multiple single-frame photographs are stitched together, and the images converted into structural drawings with an accuracy level of up to 5 cm. This authentic and undeniable data generated for every inspection that has been carried out can be stored in a centralized server or in the cloud for ensuring quick review and error-proof decision making.

The data is used for taking faster corrective measures to address potential health issues as well to validate the load-carrying capacity of the towers for changing antenna loads over a period. Cutting-edge drone technology enables creation of a repository of data for the lifecycle management of assets in an accurate manner. The results of this pilot are promising, and this disruptive method is being planned for replication on a larger scale.

With the drone helping in diagnosis, the maintenance team is pre-armed with a solution. The drone technology allows Indus to better manage its growing network of towers.

CEO Bimal Dayal says it is one of the largest back-end Network Operation Centres (NOC) in the country. The number of alarms processed is also among the highest in the country. The automation achieved here allows the team to receive information about tower sites automatically and almost instantly.

'We have just scratched the surface at this point. Where we can go with this is limited by our own dreams. Most of these towers have the potential of being run unattended and more efficiently, and bi-directionally, from a common control centre,' Dayal says. 'In fact, they can be more than just towers that send signals to cell phones. They can actually become data collection points using spectrum.'

Apart from drones, sensor technology too is being increasingly used. They are potentially capable of making the towers self-sufficient and able to self-correct using remote diagnosis for most problems. The trials for such projects are on in many telecom companies. Each location will have at least ten or twelve sensors, including cameras which will give real-time status to the back-end team. The moment this project is successful, the requirement for physical visits to a site will come down drastically, because all that would be left to do manually is to refill the diesel or do preventive maintenance. Here the monitoring team can assess potential risks and prevent them. Or if they notice and anticipate a problem, they can arrest it before it occurs.

As the number of towers grows to take care of the growing demand, the tower companies have to depend on increased automation to manage the growth. The size of telecom towers is shrinking too. The current towers transmit in the frequency of 700 MhZ. As demand grows and the market moves to 900 MhZ, the size of the towers will reduce. They will be even more compact, probably merged with the street infrastructure rather than stand as separate towers. The rising use of data means that even the demand for 900 Mhz towers cannot be met.

From IoT and sensors to data science, and finally to neuroscience, companies in India are deploying technologies that had never been considered before to know the mind of the consumer. Old tools like focus groups and surveys involved active participation by sample consumer clusters. As technologies become more sophisticated, consumer preferences will be automatically extracted by product and service sellers. Consumers may not know it and may not like it, but each of their consumption acts is leading sellers to know them better and better.

5

TRANSPORTATION AND MOBILITY

Renault India's 'Frugal Innovation'

When French automobile giant Renault began its journey in India in 2011, it was the last of the global companies to enter the country. The task for Renault India CEO Sumit Sawhney was not easy. He had to sell cars from a largely unknown brand in a market that was price sensitive but also high cost.

Reaching out to consumers meant investing heavily in automobile showrooms in cities where real estate rentals in prime locations were very high. The competitive India market for passenger cars is heavily dominated by three companies. Maruti Suzuki India, Hyundai India, and Mahindra & Mahindra together account for about 70 per cent of the passenger cars sold. Most of the good locations for car showrooms were already captured by these market leaders and by other established players like Honda, Toyota, Tata, GM, and Ford.

'When we started our operations in India, we were hardly known,' Sawhney remembers. 'India is the toughest market in the world. The expectations of the consumers are very high. Consumers want the latest and the greatest but at the lowest possible cost.'

But Renault spotted an opportunity that others had neglected. It launched a mid-sized SUV called Duster, which became a runaway hit. However, its competitors were quick to label the company as a one-hit wonder since the other cars in its stable didn't sell much. Its small car, Pulse, and sedan, Fluence, and its large-sized SUV, Koleos, did not match the performance of Duster.

Building on the success of Duster was important for Renault. The vision of the company was to enter the mini-car segment, which sells the most units by volume. Maruti Suzuki India has dominated this segment, though other companies like Hyundai and Tata had made significant inroads. For Renault to consider launching its brand in this segment was considered audacious. Sawhney says it was 'forbidden territory' for global car makers in India.

Renault saw that consumers were leaning towards an SUV look. They wanted a tough and sturdy-looking car but at the cost and with the convenience of a small vehicle, Renault's research revealed. The company then went for an aggressive look in its design and added practical features, like high ground clearance, that matched the SUV style. Cost was critical too, since this segment is most sensitive to price. Unlike the typical SUV and luxury car buyers, mini-car buyers are swayed by a price difference of less than even ₹10,000. To achieve this, Renault worked hard on a localization plan to drive down costs. Sawhney says the company achieved a 98 per cent localization level when its mini-car, KWID, hit the market in 2016. 'At launch, our spare part prices were 17 per cent lower than the competition's,' he says.

For KWID, Renault leaned on technology for three critical strategies: to make KWID affordable to buy and to drive; to build it quickly and efficiently; and finally, to excite the consumers enough to buy it.

A key objective to make the running cost low with reduced consumption of fuel was to reduce the weight of KWID. Lower weight means lower fuel for moving it, but it had to be done without compromising on the quality of steel and other materials.

Renault adopted 'Value Engineering' or 'Frugal Innovation' to reduce the unnecessary weight and cost burden of its vehicle. From the very beginning, the mandate was clear – the car has to be efficient and dynamic without compromising on safety and quality. Weight reduction of KWID was managed for every single part and also by minimizing the number of parts. For example, the inner door trim includes the mirror cover zone; there's no extra part. Making variable thickness on some trims is one example of their achievement.

Weight reduction was achieved by innovative means including the use of only three bolts on each wheel instead of the usual four, and a single windshield wiper. A reduction of about 14 kg was achieved. The weight of every small component like wiring clips was reduced and a lightweight all-aluminium engine was fitted in the car. To reduce the weight further, the wing mirrors were finished in plastic. The engineers reduced the number of screws and bolts wherever possible, and also used more plastic components under the hood. The weight of the cylinder head cover and the welds were also reduced.

Traditionally, the upper cylinder heads for engines are made of metal, but Renault discovered that they could very well be made of plastic, saving on weight without compromising on functionality. Similarly, plastic oil paint was 2 kg lighter than its metal variant.

This weight reduction of the vehicle was also possible since the new type of welding was done with advanced robotics. A small car usually requires 18–20 kg of fasteners. Renault's advanced welding technology did away with the need for these fasteners, reducing the car's weight by another 5–6 kg.

There are some welding spots can only be addressed by robots because of their accessibility, the points being beyond manual reach. The body materials of cars are getting lighter by the day, which means operations like welding require greater precision to improve the stability of the car at high speeds. Without industrial robots, many manufacturing tasks would simply be impossible, or their performance prohibitively expensive.

Also, some welding guns are too heavy for a human operator, even with dedicated manipulators. Therefore, driven by the need for increased manufacturing efficiency, the need of the hour was to move away from hard automation in favour of flexible automation. The increasing demand for more affordable and sophisticated methods of accomplishing common tasks thus created the need to use robots.

Robots are also better than operators at repetitive tasks. An operator is generally able to do the same job as a robot at the beginning of his shift, but by the end of it, the quality of results can be unpredictable as the operator may be fatigued. The welding spots are always at specific locations and that is where automation plays a great role. Automation directly helps to maintain a certain standard of quality, as robots ensure uniform application of sealant and oil, reducing avoidable wastage and resulting in direct cost savings of 10–20 per cent.

As a result of the combined effort of reducing parts and using robotics for smart welding, the weight of KWID was reduced, raising its mileage.

The second big challenge was to get consumers to experience the car without the burden of high-cost showrooms. While the company started building its network of showrooms, Renault deployed virtual reality to trigger excitement about the car among consumers.

As part of its strategic focus on enhancing the customer brand experience, Renault India created the first narrative-based 360 virtual reality (VR) film for an automotive brand in India. It narrates the story of two friends headed to a campsite in their Renault KWID. The features of the exterior and interior of the car were highlighted through the narrative, while also giving viewers their first glimpse of the car. The VR experience was shown across various activation centres (malls and dealerships) using the Oculus DK2 at booths where the car was parked for consumers to examine. However, since the interior of the car remained inaccessible to potential consumers before the launch, the 360-video served as a perfect way to get a feel of the car. This VR experience embellished the 'Live For More' tagline that the Renault KWID represents.

In a period of three months, Renault saw over 4,00,000 users visiting the Virtual Showroom website. Consumers could ask questions during their VR experience and have them answered in real-time. The KWID VR experience acted as an enabler for activations and conversations, generating a huge amount of buzz for the car. This campaign not only captivated potential consumers during their virtual experience of the car, it also led to advance orders for the KWID even before its launch.

Renault also launched an app to allow consumers to understand the car, and even make a booking for it. In some ways, the car company used mobile technology to trigger impulse-buying of a car. The Renault KWID app received over 4,00,000 downloads and more than 21,500 bookings by the end of 2016. After experiencing the features of the car, the consumer could book the car for a nominal amount using the mobile phone. Renault had allowed the booking to be done using the mobile wallet, PayTM.

'This is perhaps the first time that a consumer in India could book a car on a mobile phone without having to visit a showroom or write a cheque to a dealer,' says Sawhney. 'The VR showroom and app allowed us to reach consumers across the country, even in tier-two towns, and not just in the metros.'

*

Other players in the automobile sector are eagerly deploying similar technology to stay ahead of the new players. Maruti Suzuki in India is using robots on the shop floor in its plant in Manesar, Haryana. More than 2,000 robots work on welding, 160 in the body paint shop, and 65 in the bumper paint shop. The company says that between its plants in Manesar and Gurgaon, it has more than 5,000 robots. The company expects the level of automation to increase with time.[1]

Automation in the sector is not new since the introduction of the assembly line. But increasingly the assembly line requires less and less workers and more robots. The level of automation is increasing steadily as pressure on costs are rising. Each assembly line must also be flexible enough to ensure the introduction of new models within shorter time cycles.

From its first avatar as a pick-and-place arm (with a 'revolutionary' 6 degrees of freedom) in the 1970s, the robots of today have come a long way in changing the way vehicles are manufactured. Naturally, the advent of electronics – both in terms of capability and micro-sizing – and computing has played a huge role in this; but we must understand that nothing drives innovation in any industry as strongly as economics. On a lifetime cost scale, including charges due to fatigue, poor quality of work, workplace benefits, etc., a single robot is cheaper than the technician it replaces.[2]

*

Digital Drives Mahindra

Another automotive group, Mahindra & Mahindra, is sharpening its focus on digital technologies such as blockchain, big data analytics, IoT and even augmented reality (AR), and virtual reality to boost growth. Digitization is enabling the Mahindra group to become a customer-centric organization focused on enhancing customer value. This is being achieved through process simplification, forays into newer businesses, and by building shared economies in the interest of consumers.

For instance, M&M's auto sector is successfully deploying big data analytics for customer profiling for the XUV500. Social and digital media allow for laser-sharp targeting based on customer interests, demographics, and behavioural data. The auto sector then cross-mapped information from its customer database with the consumers' Facebook and Twitter profiles, thereby obtaining profiles based on demographics, geo-locations, psychographics, and behavioural data. The information was then used to scientifically target prospects.

Corporations like the Mahindra group are now ensuring that a digital strategy is employed to improve convenience for consumers.

Many of the processes at Mahindra that were done with physical intervention are being done online. Repair, maintenance, and servicing of vehicles require multiple calls and visits, and often there is much distrust over charges. Mahindra has converted the entire process into a digital experience.

An owner of an XUV500, the company's premium SUV, can search for a store, fix a time, and book a pick-up on the company site, www.withyouhamesha.com. This takes away the hassle of finding a trusted service provider. The consumer can identify the repairs to be done, book for the repairs, and get a cost estimate even before confirming the order. Finally, the consumer can pay online rather than make a cash transaction at the service centre. With the car picked up and delivered to the doorstep with digital booking, the consumer convenience is kept at a premium. This also increases the accountability of the company since the entire transaction is recorded digitally.

Carworkz is the first digital start-up from Mahindra First Choice Services that focuses on multi-brand car services. The team looked at various models to help it improve efficiency through the use of digital technology. The result was Carworkz. It aims to create a virtual connection between the customer and the service provider who offers various services. It allows customers to make bookings, compare costs, and review and rate service providers.

Mahindra First Choice Services has also developed a Service Cost Estimator Tool, which will help customers identify their car's problems. It then offers possible repair options across a range of service providers. This will help bring transparency to a system that is currently opaque.

Mahindra is also focused on leveraging new-generation digital technology to incubate new-age, disruptive businesses. Take a look at Trringo. The farm equipment sector of the company sensed an opportunity in the tractor rental space when it realized there was a high seasonal demand for tractors from non-owners. The latter had to depend on local resources and channels to rent tractors, which was not very reliable due to various factors, including demand and supply imbalances, non-availability of the desired equipment, and social anomalies.

The business realized that this gap – primarily due to lack of supply – could be bridged by creating a rental model similar to that of Uber, but enhanced by a network of franchisees who ensure on-ground supply and support, and enable crop-based solutions. The team thus created Trringo, an organized rental business for farm equipment, aimed at helping small farmers across India who may not have the necessary funds to buy the equipment. This has helped create a common pool of resources which can be accessed through a digitally-enabled model by farmers who need these vital resources. Trringo is brand-agnostic, which increases the scope of the model.

SmartShift is a new-age Mahindra business that effectively leverages technology. It is essentially a digital mobility start-up that functions as a technology-enabled marketplace for intra-city logistics. A load-exchange platform, it connects business owners with reliable transporters based on shipment, size, weight, and other requirements, making local transportation relatively easy. The solution is supported by a web app and a call centre interface.

*

Uber and Ola's New Road

Ride-sharing or ride-booking companies have already transformed the way people commute in cities. While Uber is leading the way globally, it has strong footprint in India, where it competes with Ola Cabs. Ride-sharing companies are not only changing the experience for commuters, but for car makers too.

To put things in perspective, as late as in 2012, ride-sharing in India was largely occasioned by a combination of paucity of transport and the goodwill of the original passenger(s). Previous attempts at ride-sharing services were hampered by the limitations of the technology of the time and the lack of investors interested in funding them, and had failed. But with Uber launching UberPool, and Ola, OlaShare, the scene was turned on its head. These ride-sharing programmes have seen over a million rides booked in the past two years. Uber claims that UberPool has resulted in the saving of over a million passenger-kilometres and over 50,000 litres of fuel within a short while of its launch. For a planet that is struggling to replenish its natural resources, these numbers – if true – are heartening indeed.

The Uber India president says the company has completed 500 million rides as of July 2017.[3] Ola is estimated to be doing over 6 million rides weekly.[4]

As a rising number of commuters begin to use ride-sharing, the concept of personal ownership of a transport vehicle is changing. According to many estimates, an average car owned by an individual is parked about 95 per cent of the time, and driven only 5 per cent of the time.[5] In a ride-sharing car, the ratio is almost the reverse. The car is being used almost all the time and is therefore less of a burden on public space.

As this trend rises, consumers will be loath to buying cars and will become more dependent on ride-sharing services that run on technology platforms. Car makers who fear a fall in demand for cars in India are partnering with ride-sharing companies. The market for fleet-owned cars has grown from 2–3 per cent of sales to almost 20 per cent. This figure will rise further.

Ownership of cars will shift from individuals to institutions. In the US, Lyft has a partnership with General Motors. In India, Tata Motors has begun a partnership with Uber to sell cars. Drivers who want to buy cars for Uber will get flexible and customized financing options from Tata Motors Finance and Tata Capital. Since every Uber driver is an entrepreneur, Tata Business Support services will even help newcomers in setting up their business.

Tata's competition, the Mahindra group, has tied up with Ola Cabs to sell 40,000 cars over two years. Chairman Anand Mahindra says his group is ready to make the most of the disruption caused by ride-sharing companies. Mahindra will sell cars for 'access' as well as for the traditional 'acquisition' model of personal buying. This means that soon every second buyer of a passenger car could be a company. Individual buyers would only make for 50 per cent of the market in the future.

The next step for ride-sharing companies is to make the commute as personal as possible. Their objective is to help the passenger feel as much at home in a hired car as he would in his own. An initiative in this direction is Ola Play. Commuters of prime rides will be able to use their app and their mobile phone to connect with the car they book to take control of the entertainment within the car. As a result, the music and video in the car will be run by the passenger, and not the driver.

The vehicles will have an in-car console, including a screen for the passenger, much like in an airline. However, the controls will lie with the phone of the passenger. This personalized offering will ensure that the passenger does not miss the choice of a personal vehicle and is not alienated by the music that is usually played by the driver.

Globally, Uber is taking the ride-sharing model into two new sectors. One is food delivery. And the second is trucking and logistics. Building on its network of drivers, UberEATS is the food-delivery platform that has started in the US and Australia, and will soon be expanded to other countries. It has begun operations in India too.

Building on its ride-matching algorithms, UberEATS matches drivers to the nearest restaurant. The algorithm ensures that the driver arrives just in time to pick up the food and delivers it just in time for the consumer's satisfaction. The menu is designed to offer instant food with a choice of items that ensures that delivery time is minimal. Instead of consumers spending minutes scrolling several menus, UberEATS helps them narrow their selection with a strict time deadline in mind.

Essentially, the basic Uber app and the UberEATS app do the same task. This effort is broken into four elements: identification of the user's location; directing the driver to reach the user's destination; identification of the best routes which will take minimum time; constant updating of information from all mapping and traffic information software. Other algorithms calculate the fare, which is a combination of distance travelled and time taken.

Soon Uber will launch trucking solutions for long-haul freight. An approach similar to the one it has for passengers will be applied to freight too. Uber will use its algorithms to match shippers with carriers to bring a higher level of efficiency using independent drivers and trucking companies.

*

The protectionist attitudes of the early governments in the decades following Independence slowed the transportation industry in India. Much like the America of Henry Ford, buyers in India had a limited choice when it came to personal vehicles – it was either the bulky workhorse, the Ambassador, or the cramped Fiat 1100/Premier Padmini. Things were slightly better in the two-wheeler space with a few more options, but production was often slowed down by labour issues, and delivery was often many months after booking.

Things looked up when the then government of India entered into a joint venture with Japan's Suzuki, introducing in India the Maruti 800. It wasn't until the crisis of 1991, however, when the central government relaxed the rules for investment and manufacturing that other car makers started to consider

India as a viable market. Prices remained high until these car makers were able to set up their own plants, most of them in and around Chennai, and reduced their dependence on costly imports from offshore sites. Even as a consolidation spree was happening across the world, car makers like Chevrolet, Fiat, Volkswagen, and Nissan rebadged some of their most successful designs for Indian buyers.

As a traditionally slow adopter of technology, it is understandable why the Indian market is yet to be as demanding as the markets in the West when it comes to advanced safety features. Airbags, for instance, which are mandatory in several EU and American countries, are an optional, 'premium' accessory in India. But in the past few years, driven by competition, car makers have been earnestly trying to use technology to reduce their production and service times. However, with cost being a primary concern for buyers, most manufacturers wait until a new technology has become cheaper before introducing it in the Indian market.

In the past ten years alone, the sales volume of cars and two-wheelers have doubled, from 1.5 million units to 3.4 million units, and from 7.6 million units to 18.8 million units, respectively.[6]

However, unfortunately, roads haven't been expanded proportionately to accommodate the new vehicles. With fuel prices also doubling (petrol from ₹36/litre in 2005 to ₹72/litre in 2016), and with parking facilities still a novel concept in many popular areas, the focus has shifted to smaller, more fuel-efficient cars and on-demand services like Uber and Ola.

A pioneer of home-grown small-car designs, the Reva Electric Car Company was formed in 1994 as a joint venture between the Maini group and the Amerigon Electric Vehicle

Technologies Inc. Their first commercial product, the Reva, was ahead of its times and did not become a mass-market leader, but it did certainly set the conversation going in the right direction. It was perhaps priced too high for a price-conscious market, with the result that people preferred 'bigger' hatchbacks because they offered 'more space per rupee'.

The Tata Nano, born of Ratan Tata's unwavering vision for a cheap, safe car, was another turning point in India's automotive history. While the jury is still out on the model's profitability (it is no longer a one-lakh-rupee car, having been upgraded with automatic transmission, AC, and power steering in its high-end variant) it reinforced the industry's focus on small cars that can be manoeuvred easily on Indian roads. In the past few years, Chevrolet's Spark, Nissan's Micra, Datsun's redi-GO, and Maruti's new Alto have been fighting a tough battle for a dominant share of this pie.

Ola, which entered the market much before Uber did, has been one of the rising stars in the aggregator space. One of its key innovations was the Ola Auto, which enabled a user to hail an auto-rickshaw with the app. Ola Auto promised its riders authentic point-to-point billing, cashless payment and no last-minute 'surcharges' by the driver. Another project, Ola Shuttle, had to be shelved when it ran afoul of local Road Transport Office rules.

Start-ups have evolved from simply adapting proven, Western ideas to creating new, India-specific solutions. For instance, redBus proved that it was possible to bring order to the chaos of the highly disorganized long-distance bus-travel ecosystem in the country. Where there had once been a quota system for travel agents and booking offices (and an agent would have to call the operator's office in the source city to determine the availability of tickets), there was now an online ticket management system that allowed you to book tickets using just a computer or a mobile phone. It brought in an operational efficiency unseen till then, with operators now being able to maintain a real-time inventory of seats and being able to offer tickets point-to-point.

Even the behemoth of Indian transport industry, the Indian Railways, is now embracing technology for more than just ticket management. You can order food en route, request the cabins or restrooms to be cleaned, entertain yourself, and make bookings on the fly.

The impetus given to city planning by the present government as part of its Smart Cities initiative stresses on transportation, mobility, and last-mile connectivity. Some cities are already ahead of the rest, with their dedicated bus corridors (the Bus Rapid Transit System in Ahmedabad, Indore, Surat, and Pune), metro rail systems (in Bangalore, Chennai, Kochi, New Delhi, and Kolkata), monorail (in Mumbai) and suburban rail systems (in Kolkata, Chennai, and Mumbai). Other cities are expected to join the list soon, with many projects under way.

The invention of the steam engine, which had kicked off the First Industrial Revolution in the nineteenth century, turned the paradigms for both manufacturing and transportation on their head. In fact, one of the first things we associate with automobile manufacturing is the assembly line. It is interesting to note that the concept, in perhaps a slower form, existed as far back as in the 1300s, when the Venetian Arsenal could kit out an entire battle-ready ship in a day!

Modern manufacturing, it is widely believed, kicked off with Henry Ford's adoption of the assembly line system for the Model T. With sales doubling practically every year in the first few years, it was imperative that the company's output had to scale up to meet the demand, and it did. In just nineteen years, Ford produced and sold over 15 million Model T units. While the competitors were still putting together their cars by hand – an expensive and time-consuming process – Ford's production line churned out a car every hour!

Soon, the exception became the norm. By the 1930s, manufacturers all over the world used assembly lines and were competing with each other in increasing productivity without compromising on quality. The rapid advancements in automobile engineering and an industry shift towards 'planned, annual obsolescence' meant that the assembling units needed to be modular, capable of being shuffled so as to put together different variants or even different models without significant downtime while retooling. The post-war consumerism, driven by patriotism in America, reassertion in Asia and reconstruction in Europe, saw the automobile industry more than double in fifteen years (1945–1960), and again in the next ten (1960–70).

Customer choice and comfort became an important differentiator among the brands. Even as the refrigerator itself was starting to find traction in the public imagination, companies sprung up offering air-conditioning in cars. In 1939, the Packard Motor Company offered after-market air-conditioning and heating units that could be installed in most models. While the initial models were bulky and space-consuming, the later models were integrated into the chassis itself and were significantly more efficient.

The introduction of computing devices into the design, manufacture and operations of a car significantly altered the landscape of this industry, as much as the wartime advances in material sciences and aerodynamics had. The production process in many factories was almost completely automatic by this time, with workers used mainly to man the switches or handle tasks too gentle or demanding of dexterity (such as splicing wires, fitting windshields, etc.) for machines to execute. In recent years, fibreglass has been used to replace parts of the vehicle to reduce both cost and weight.

The year 1968 saw the introduction of micro-computing devices in the automobile itself when Volkswagen started to use computer-controlled electronic fuel injection systems in its models to comply with fuel-emission directives. In 1969, Ford introduced a computer-assisted anti-braking system. A few years later, the world's first self-driving car, Carnegie Mellon University's Navlab 1, was rolled out. Luxury brands such as BMW and Mercedes now have variants that can be remotely accessed by the manufacturers for troubleshooting and repairs, and for tracking and disabling the vehicle remotely in the event of its theft or incapacitation of the driver. The manufacturer of the LoJack Stolen Vehicle Recovery system – which helps locate a vehicle by means of a silent transceiver hidden within – claims a 90 per cent success rate.

Given the transformation of the car from a simple point-to-point enabler to an almost self-contained unit that combined entertainment, comfort, and intelligence, it is no wonder that towards the end of the century, even well-planned cities found themselves struggling with too many cars on the roads and too much pollution in the air.

The innovations in transportation and mobility of late have tried to address these concerns. For those of us who are environment-friendly, there are now hybrid cars available – hybrid in the sense that they run both on fossil fuel and renewable (or at least non-toxic) alternatives such as hydrogen-fuel cells, electricity, etc. It is interesting to note that despite the investments (on paper, at least) that have gone into researching 'cleaner, greener' vehicles, the pace of commercial adaptation has been slower than it ought to be, given both the production technology now available to us and the urgent need to stem the toll transportation is taking on the planet. Elon Musk's Tesla is one of the most famous drivers of cleaner technology. The new Model 3 is bringing Tesla closer to creating a popular mass market vehicle.

In India, the government is planning a big push for electric vehicles. The National Electric Mobility Mission Plan has earmarked a 2020 sales target of 7 million annually for electric and hybrid cars.

Energy Minister Piyush Goyal says he wants to sell only electric cars by 2030.[7]

This will save the country $60 billion in fuel costs. A series of policy measures and subsidies are being rolled out to encourage electric car production. Elon Musk is among the global leaders to cheer India on in this effort.[8]

If fewer people are buying new cars these days, it is because the focus has shifted from 'ownership' to 'hiring'. Although radio cabs have been around since the '50s, their use was often subject to limitations – the passenger had to call the local cab operator to request a ride, and there were no guarantees as to timelines or quality. And in many countries, two-way radio communications itself was barred for civilian use. Later, in the early '90s, companies experimented with computer-assisted systems. These, however, still required a human operator to make the right connections.

The arrival of Uber, which is now almost a verb by itself, in 2010 dramatically altered the business of hiring cabs. For the passenger, the experience was a novel relief: you used a mobile phone to call a cab to your location, the billing would be computerized, and the fare could be paid in cash or electronically. There was no longer the need to haggle over the fare, and the drivers had higher accountability. From an operational point of view, Uber had the best of both worlds – it left the responsibility of ownership, compliance, and maintenance to the operator while collecting a commission on every ride booked through its platform.

Between 2010 and 2016, Uber expanded operations to cover 550+ cities in sixty-six countries, claiming over 1 million trips a day by the end of 2016. Uber's success has been replicated across the world and has spawned many 'inspired' ventures. This has not gone down well with the local operators in many places who haven't signed on, leading to disruptive protests that may, arguably and counter-intuitively, benefit Uber in the long run. Uber itself is testing out a concept that has, until recently, been the stuff of sci-fi novels – driverless cars. Safety concerns exist, of course, especially over the decision matrices when dealing with unpredictable road or passenger behaviour.

Taxis are, of course, not the sole means of public transport. China recently unveiled its super bus as a possible solution to its problems of traffic congestion in urban areas. However, the idea has been challenged by operational constraints. The Transit Elevated Bus as the super bus is called, which straddles three lanes of traffic like a giant bug, allowing smaller cars to travel underneath its carriage, requires a special track that is proving to be a headache to construct. If this succeeds, however, it will be a far cheaper alternative to building suburban metros or rail networks.

The Hyperloop, first proposed by Elon Musk, is expected to be the next big game changer in fixed-route public transport. This system transports pressure-controlled 'pods' that contain passengers over a reduced-pressure tube. In principle, by reducing friction and pressure, not only can the speed be safely increased to 970 km per hour, but the wear and tear normally associated with such high speeds can be reduced too. In India, a Hyperloop system has been proposed to be built between Chennai and Mumbai, passing through Bengaluru.

Metros and local-transit rail services are themselves adapting to the new demands. Most trains are almost completely automated now, with the driver expected to simply hold the Dead Man's Switch as a fail-safe, while the onboard/centralized computer adjusts speed, air-conditioning, doors, and stoppages. The service operators use sophisticated programs and deep-data algorithms to identify load patterns, forecast traffic, handle maintenance and breakdowns, and alter schedules without compromising on safety. And to increase passenger output, layouts are continuously optimized and electronic tickets (using NFC/RFID technology) that do not need to be recharged over the counter have been introduced. Given that one of the biggest challenges to the adoption of public mass-transit systems is in making it the easiest option for a commuter, these steps definitely seem to be in the right direction.

India has varied transport needs. From self-owned cars to car sharing, the transition has been rapid for consumers. For manufacturers, the challenges are much more. They are facing faster obsolescence, strict emission norms, and reduced ownership. As governments invest in mass transport, demand for private vehicles will not rise commensurate with the buying population. The focus on, and investment in, electric vehicles is increasing. Promotion of electric vehicles could further change the way vehicles are made and used in India. Already the government has announced its intention to sell only electric cars by 2030. What is sure is that Indians will be moving about in transportation systems that utilize almost every new technology that becomes popular in the world.

6

HEALTHCARE AND DIAGNOSTICS

Neil Harbisson was born with achromatopsia or complete colour blindness. After many years of suffering, he learnt that there may be a solution to colour blindness. He had a sensor implanted in his skull with an antenna jutting out over his head. The antenna and sensor together read the different wavelengths of light and converts them into colour. The sensor then sends vibrations into his skull, which he then feels as sounds. As a result, he 'hears' colours rather than sees them. Harbisson is called a cyborg because of this device in his head. He represents another step towards humans using technological devices to improve or repair their physical or mental abilities. From pacemakers to antennas is not a very big step. But it does look strange to see a human being with an antenna sticking out of the head. When I met Neil in May 2017, he was sure that wearing an antenna would not be abnormal in the near future. 'I am not wearing technology, I am technology,' he says.

Humans have invested in technology to enhance, improve, and recreate their body and mind for centuries. Investment in personal health has been driven by global pharmaceutical giants, medical equipment makers as well as government and privately funded research. The human genome project required investment of over $2.7 billion. Gene-editing is allowing scientists to remove elements of the DNA that cause terminal diseases. Currently, governments allow editing of genes to remove illness. But it is also possible to add elements to our genes that can give us unnatural abilities.

Health technology has two broad strains of development. One set of technologies is like gene-editing or cancer research that impacts everyone in every country. Another set of technologies consists of what is applied in the regional context. While a UK-born Harbisson can afford to get an implant for his colour blindness, he also has the luxury of converting himself into an art project. However, for the poor in places like India, China or east Africa, blindness caused by cataract is virtually untreatable. Mostly this is because medical help is difficult to access and also unaffordable. For such regions, simple innovations that can be scaled up to treat hundreds of thousands at an affordable price make a big impact.

In India, the health technology developments and usage are more aligned to solving local problems than to tackling generic issues that plague the world.

*

Google's AI-first Strategy

Google has launched a big effort on different fronts using artificial intelligence as a platform in India. The solutions it is offering range across different sectors. CEO Sundar Pichai's 'AI First' strategy is playing out well. 'In an AI-first world, we are rethinking all our products,' Pichai said, at Google's annual meeting in May 2017. This means that most of the products and services that Google creates will have AI-driven innovation embedded in them.

Its early success has been in healthcare, in its focus on curing retinal blindness. Here is a note that Google's product manager Lily Peng shared with me for this book.

Artificial intelligence and machine learning in diabetic eye disease detection

Diabetic patients are at risk for a form of blindness known as diabetic retinopathy, with nearly 415 million diabetic patients at risk worldwide. If detected early, proper treatment can help curb its detrimental effects, but if unchecked it can lead to irreversible blindness. To detect this disease, specialists examine the back of the patient's eye, which indicates the presence and severity of the disease. However, this process is time consuming, and is often unavailable to millions of likely patients who live in remote areas.

Three years ago, Google began working closely with Indian medical organizations such as the Sankara Eye Hospitals and the Aravind Medical Research Foundation, using technology to reduce the time it takes to detect cases of diabetic retinopathy.

Using machine learning, Google trained a deep neural network using 1,28,000 retinal scans, enabling the algorithm to discern patterns that enabled the system to achieve high sensitivity (correctly identifying the presence of the disease), and specificity (correctly identifying the absence of the disease).

While the initial sets of results have been heartening, much work still needs to be done before the system is ready for field implementation. For example, in India, Google is working with local medical organizations on adapting the algorithm to grading the scales and performance metrics relevant to the populations they treat – these vary subtly across the world, and it is important for the algorithm to be sensitive in some cases, and specific in others.

The repercussions of AI-assisted medical treatment has the propensity of extending even beyond the operation theatre – it could even be used to refine and optimize integration with the EMR and existing equipment like retinal cameras.

ML has the capability of helping extend the reach of healthcare providers and bringing high quality care to everyone, especially rural and underserved communities where there is a shortage of experts. Healthcare providers will need to play a key role here for successful adoption of these technologies. For example, in the case of our work in diabetic retinopathy, as the algorithms detect more people that require treatment, the healthcare systems will also have to adapt so that they can manage the increase in patients who need treatment.

Thus, ML's true potential, will only be realized when deployed in partnership with healthcare providers.

Apart from healthcare, there are many other sectors in which the AI-first strategy is rolling out. In July 2017, Google acquired Halli Labs, a start-up in Bengaluru which focuses on AI-based solutions.[1] The company has also announced that it is mentoring many start-ups in AI in India. These include SigTuple, whose work on AI-based diagnostics is profiled later in the book. 'The start-ups were shortlisted for their unique value proposition and use of AI and ML to build high-impact solutions for Internet users and the government's flagship initiative Digital India. We look forward to working with them over the next six months,' said Google India programme manager, Paul Ravindranath, in a statement.[2] Expect Google to acquire more such companies in India.

*

Health technology covers an entire range of products and services employed in the field of health management. To avoid a popular misconception, the healthcare industry referred to in this chapter is a superset of both the medical field and the technological advancements that are used in curative, restorative, palliative, and preventive treatments. A well-developed nation typically has a well-developed healthcare system, with proper delivery and reporting mechanisms in place.

One of the earliest applications of technology in this field was the use of X-rays. Madame Curie's husband, Pierre Curie, contributed his own genius through the discovery of piezoelectricity (production of electricity through pressure on certain materials), which would eventually help in the generation of ultrasonic-frequency sound waves which are inaudible to the human ear. Ultrasonic imaging would end up being one of the most revolutionary tools available to the diagnostician.

Magnetic Resonance Imaging (MRI), another non-invasive diagnostic tool, was invented in 1971, building on the research and findings in the field of magnetics and resonance since the late 1940s.

Many of the machines we see these days can be considered to be direct descendants of these technologies, employing them in one way or another. As the computing industry grew, becoming more advanced and flexible, companies discovered ways of connecting equipment to terminals, enabling faster diagnoses and recording of a patient's state of health at different points of time.

In the past two decades, driven principally by the human need to preserve such records, the healthcare industry has expanded to bring in more products and services. If, at one time, the term 'healthcare' encompassed only purely medical elements, it now covers ancillary elements such as insurance providers, analytics engines, research departments, device engineers, patients, doctors, wearable technology, at-home/consumer devices, and even socio-legal frameworks.

For instance, electronic health records – which were considered an emerging application as late as in 2009 – are now one of the key drivers for the next generation in healthcare. By standardizing medical histories and reports, it is now possible for hospitals and pharmaceutical companies to keep track of results and monitor them for side-effects. More importantly, though, it has helped save lives because a care provider no longer needs to wait to have a critical patient's file scanned and sent across.

Wearable technology, such as blood-glucose monitors or pH-monitoring bandages, have reduced the load on clinics without compromising on the patient's lifestyle. There are now pacemakers available that can store and transmit data to processing centres for analysis.

Clinical laboratories have also gained out of the advancements in technology. It is no longer necessary to have a data-entry operator keying in the results of reports manually; most modern institutions have equipment that runs tests and prepares reports without ever needing a human hand to guide it (other than to decide which tests to run, of course). The time needed to run each test has been reduced too, thanks to improvements in processes and increased bandwidth.

Some of the more advanced commercially-available wheelchairs these days were science fiction in the 1960s, and are capable of voice- or gesture-controlled movement, climbing, accelerating or braking, intelligently manoeuvring around obstacles, monitoring the patients' vitals, dispensing medicines, etc. Precision-tooled artificial limbs are already available, while research into more capable robotic limbs, tied into the body's nervous system just as a natural limb would be, are already beginning to yield results.[3]

Prohibitive costs and import rules – not to mention sanctions on their sale to India – had held back India in the healthcare sector, at least technologically, until the late 1980s. Only a handful of hospitals had modern equipment that was on par with the best of the rest of the world; others had to make do with knock-offs and previous-generation technology.

That's no longer the case. India is now one of the preferred medical tourism destinations in the world. For instance, a surgery carried out at one of the top Indian hospitals would still be 30–50 per cent cheaper than in America, and that's including the travel fare (a heart-valve replacement, for instance, would cost around $2,00,000 in the US, but only around $8,000 in India!). Many Indian doctors have also studied or practised abroad, with the result that they are bringing in best practices and a more tech-friendly/-dependent approach than was the case earlier.[4]

In the past few years, with governments across the world freeing up controls on transfer of such technology, hospitals in India have also begun to invest heavily in modern equipment.

With the exception of electronic health records – which the past two regimes have been mulling over – everything else that's available to the Western world is also available in India. While this may have resulted in runaway appreciation of costs, some experts feel that economies of scale should kick in at some point of time and lead to a more natural price structure.

One of the key movements that's perhaps more prominent in India these days than anywhere else in the world is the push for remote medical care. Envisioned as standalone units in remote locations which are connected to a central network of hospitals and processing centres, this system will help patients consult with doctors who are physically present elsewhere, just as they would in person. Even diagnostic tests can be run on the patient.

Analytics, as in the West, is also making its presence felt in the country. Microsoft recently tied up with Hyderabad-based LV Prasad Eye Institute for use of its Azure AI-based analytics platform to mine insights from millions of patient data points. The expectation is that by correlating medical histories and conditions to geography and economic indicators, doctors will be able to predict more accurately the chances of success of eye surgeries at a patient-specific level, and thus be better placed to advise their patients.[5]

In India, the medical efforts in research and technology have been more focused on affordable solutions. Low-tech solutions that work in remote villages are as much celebrated as low-cost solutions that the middle classes can make the most of. Medical technology that works on scale, cost, and durability has always been welcome. The stunning success of the fight against polio was about creating the simplest of delivery solutions for hundreds of millions of children. By giving drops of vaccine rather than injectables, the fight was revolutionized. Even untrained workers could reach out to poor families across the country. A nurse with injectables, taking the necessary anti-infection measures, was not needed in millions of locations.

In recent years, while the hardware for technology has been imported, the big effort has been with respect to access-based solutions.

Private hospital chains allowed many city dwellers to get world-class treatment at a fraction of the cost of global services at their doorstep. Technology is being used to create solutions that can take medicare even to the homes of city dwellers. The idea is to reduce the pressure on private hospitals, who are staggering under their own success. However, demand still heavily outstrips supply of healthcare services.

*

Fortis' Connected Care

There are several areas where technology has contributed to healthcare. The increased adoption of telemedicine, health information systems, electronic health records, mobile health, and web-based services have amplified the use of hospital data and enabled mapping of digitization trends in health information and electronic medical records. One of the key consequences of health transformation through technology is the ability to provide access to the best healthcare to a larger segment of the population at an affordable price.

Technology is a cost-effective way to connect remote clinics and small nursing homes with limited skills and facilities with larger, full-service hospitals and specialists. In urban areas and tier-two towns, IT has improved patient management practices by digitizing manual processes.

Many of the major healthcare providers in India are now gearing up to make use of the advances in connectivity, miniaturization, and information management protocols to streamline their operations, bringing in efficiency and, more importantly to those who need their services, convenience in the form of reports, services, follow-ups, etc. One of the companies I spoke to, Fortis Healthcare, stressed on the investments they were making in these areas.

Fortis Healthcare launched its initiative, 'One Fortis', through the implementation of Project F1, an organization-wide ERP programme in 2015. Project F1 is an Oracle-based ERP system that unifies the critical business functions of finance, supply chain, and human resources to improve efficiencies. In December 2015, Fortis formally kicked off a project to design and deploy an Organizational Hospital Information System (OHIS) across all Fortis hospitals in a record twenty-seven months. Further, Fortis is also using telemedicine to expand its reach exponentially. Its E-ICU brand 'Critinext' replicates and orchestrates a high-order intensive care environment at a remote hospital from a central e-hub that is manned by specialists, who enable 24x7 patient surveillance at the remote facility. At present, over 400 beds in twelve cities are being served through this arrangement.

The Fortis mobile health (mHealth) application, MyFortis, launched last year, is extremely handy and useful. It allows patients to find a Fortis hospital closest to them and book an appointment with the appropriate doctor. It also provides updated information on the latest available health offerings at various Fortis hospitals, allows patients to view the credentials of the doctors, and the available time slots that can be booked. Appointments can be fixed and paid for either by cash/card/ online or on arrival.

An extension of the same platform, Fortis 24x7, provides an immediate interface between doctors and patients. It allows for a consultation to take place over the telephone for immediate advice. The app ensures that doctors are available 24x7, 365 days of the year.

Based on the findings of a study it voluntarily undertook, Fortis took a 'public cloud only' approach which improved user perception and removed dependence on its company-run data centres. Fortis moved nearly forty applications to Microsoft Azure, including its HIS, Oracle Supply Chain, databases, application servers, several line-of-business applications, and the intranet. All this was achieved in just eight months. By not spending time on micro-managing infrastructure, Fortis claims it was able to focus on its primary business goals.

Patient Reported Outcome Measures (PROMs) reflect the voice of the consumer, ensuring greater objectivity in the entire initiative. The International Consortium for Health Outcomes Measurement (ICHOM) standard set for coronary artery disease, implemented at Fortis Escorts Heart Institute (FEHI), measures and monitors clinical outcomes for Coronary Artery Bypass Graft (CABG) and Percutaneous Coronary Intervention (PCI, PTCA). Clinical outcomes of additional procedures such as Total Knee Replacement, Radiation Oncology, Endoscopic Retrograde Cholangio Pancreatography (ERCP), and Maternal and Child Health are also being monitored and will be added in phases in the near future.

As Malvinder Mohan Singh, co-owner of Fortis, says, 'It is true when we say that whoever takes that first step gets the lead. In the times to come, we will see technology becoming a critical factor in driving the competitive edge across hospital service delivery in India. Mobility and cloud adoption will become the standard norm and will open new frontiers in enabling wider and faster access to healthcare, radically transforming the engagement model and benefiting patients across the world.'

As part of this effort to bring in more transparency, the Fortis Healthcare website has been updated with FEHI, CABG, and PTCA data till June 2016, enabling a two-year comparison. In addition, as patient and graft survival is the most accepted clinical outcome parameter for measuring the success of a kidney transplant, recipients are followed up through consultations and check-ups at regular intervals to assess their general well-being and the functioning of their transplanted kidney. Information on all these can be accessed at http://www.fortishealthcare.com/Clinical-Outcomes.

*

Practo, a company started in 2008, is one of the key service providers in the field now. From helping patients 'discover' the best doctors in their disciplines to now providing an entire ecosystem in healthcare practice management, Practo's ascendance has been rapid these past few years. Patients and practitioners alike can now register appointments, schedule follow-ups (or be reminded for the same), and keep a digital record of their treatments and prescriptions. Shared infrastructure keeps the costs down to affordable rates – in fact, Practo was not charging any of its patients for using its service at the time of writing this book.

What this does is provide for data at a level that was only on the wish list a decade ago. Pharmaceutical companies, doctors, and other healthcare providers can now base their decisions on incontrovertible, clear-cut data instead of (educated, charitable) guesses that might still put a patient at some risk of a wrong course of action.

Robotics

Robotic surgery is a minimally invasive surgical technique, similar to laparoscopic or 'button-hole' surgery wherein a surgical robot manipulates specialized surgical instruments on the command of the surgeon. Robotic surgery, or robot-assisted surgery, allows doctors to perform many types of complex procedures with more precision, flexibility, and control, than is possible with conventional techniques. By using this platform, the surgeon is able to carry out highly complex dissections and reconstructions in a 3-D environment, which has a direct bearing on the functional outcome. Human factors such as hand tremors, visual acuity, limitations of human hand movements, etc. are negated by the device.

In India, many of the top hospitals have started using robots to assist their surgeons. It helps their case that educated people are aware of the benefits of such a course of action and don't mind paying for a machine to be a part of their operations. The Kokilaben Hospital in Mumbai, for instance, claims to have performed over 1,000 robot-assisted surgeries within just forty-eight months of its launch in 2009.

Ajay Godara, director at Ennovate Lab LLP, in an interview to ElectronicsForU, said he expects robots to soon play a bigger role in the earlier stages of healthcare itself.[6] With AI systems becoming more capable these days, it is only a matter of time before robots are assigned routine rubric-based tasks like first-level diagnosis.

Intuitive Surgical's *da Vinci* robot was invented in 2003 and is currently the only one of its kind available worldwide. This robot is used in cardiac, thoracic, paediatric, and general surgery disciplines. It received approval from the Food and Drug Administration in the US in 2000. For patients, the biggest benefit of robot-assisted surgery is its minimal invasiveness. It is also performed with better precision and ensures minimal blood loss as compared with standard open surgeries. The other benefits are reduced hospital stay and faster healing, less post-operative pain and less need for pain medication, fewer complications, such as surgical site infections, and a quicker return to normal activities and work for the patient.

*

Max Healthcare: ICU at Home

India's hospital bed-to-patient ratio is among the worst in the world. While India has many world-class hospitals, their concentration is in urban areas. Moreover, even in urban areas, hospitals do not have the space to cater to all patients. One of the key innovations being developed is out-of-hospital services, more commonly termed as 'home care'. This is currently a ₹11,000-crore market in India. It is expected to grow at a compound annual growth rate (CAGR) of 20 per cent, the highest amongst all healthcare services. The demand for such services is being driven by the increase in India's ageing population and the significant increase in non-communicable diseases (over 60 per cent of the total disease burden).

Patients suffering from chronic illnesses like heart failure, respiratory failure, and Alzheimer's may not require hospitalization but continuous monitoring, which can be easily provided at home. In India, the joint-family structure is slowly fading away, making home-based healthcare an imperative.

However, the demand for home healthcare is increasing not only due to changes in population and disease patterns, but also due to changes in medical processes and technology. Today, close to 70 per cent (by volume) of all healthcare procedures can be conducted at home and at lower costs; this is further supported by the fact that patient recovery rates are 30 per cent better at home than in hospitals.[7]

In the last three to five years, India has seen many new entrants in this area, along with significant investments in business functions and technology. Among the large groups, Max Healthcare has invested aggressively in providing out-of-hospital services using connected technology. The current components of the demand landscape (both technology-led and otherwise) include:

Retail customers: These include individual customers or families requiring services like:

- Wellness and wellness-focused wearables
- Convenience-focused services at home
- Palliative care at home, post-surgery

- Chronic care management
- Critical care support to reduce expenses/end-of-life care
- Reaching out to doctors (e-consults/e-prescriptions)
- Health records and information
- Emergency support

Group customers: These include corporations, schools, RWAs, clubs, etc., which are focusing on providing health benefits/ services to their members. The key demand areas include:
- On-site health facilities
- Employee health programme management
- Emergency services

Clinicians: Clinicians are seeking services to stay better connected with their existing patients as well as to reach out to additional prospects. The key services they require include:
- Tracking and monitoring the health of their patients
- Medical information/data of patients
- E-consult and e-prescription

Employees: Home-health employees, unlike regular healthcare employees, operate remotely and mostly as individuals (unlike a team in hospitals), hence their needs include:
- Scheduling and managing services (including locations)
- Access to patient medical information and history
- Operational ability to complete the service (registration, billing, etc.)
- Performance dashboards

Healthcare providers: These are organizations providing home-health/out-of-hospital services; they not only require the complete operating platform but also an ecosystem to tie up with multiple other service providers. They require:

- End-to-end operating platform, integrating all stakeholders (including clinicians)
- Standardization and adherence to clinical protocols
- Administrative management for a remote workforce

Out-of-hospital players are creating technology ecosystems to enable themselves to provide the entire range of these services. Since it is impractical for players to specialize in all services, the only way to cater to changing customer needs is to create a technology ecosystem where a company can not only provide its own services but also tie up with other B2B providers to extend their services to its patients.

Max has tied up with India's leading fitness band providers to integrate wellness and healthcare to enable continuous monitoring. Doctor referral programmes have been initiated, wherein patients can book appointments (e-consults) or see previous details from the wellness app. Customer vitals can be synced via fitness bands, which can be used to escalate emergency cases.

For patients with critical care needs, Max is working on special services called ICU@Home.

These services track and monitor patient vitals through connected devices to create an ICU-like environment at home itself. The data that is collected is shared on a real-time basis with the treating clinicians, as the need may be.

Additionally, for on-site health facilities for group customers, Max is introducing a state-of-the-art tele-medicine solution for doctor triage, non-invasive diagnostics and health-service kiosks. Portable devices, including 12-lead ECG and digital stethoscopes, are fully equipped to capture more than six different vitals of patients. It also allows ease of remote doctor consults and prescriptions.

Buttons are being integrated into Max's apps to trigger requests for ambulances, updating of family members, detection of GPS location, and arranging of connect calls with a doctor. During an emergency, the app will be able to inform family members of the patient without needing any manual intervention.

With the demographics needs, advancement in clinical technologies, and customer demand, home healthcare in India is likely to see a significant growth trajectory for the next five to ten years. And, as in most other areas, technology will play a key role in making it happen.

*

While healthcare service providers are offering new solutions based on connectivity, the pharmaceutical sector is witnessing its own range of start-ups and solutions.

First, let's take a look at how the process of discovering medicines began.

It all started on a summer afternoon in 1928 when Prof. Alexander Fleming left a petri dish uncapped, forgot to close the window of his laboratory, and left town for five weeks, giving mother nature time to work her miracles. On his return, he found that something had secreted a mould (later identified as Penicillin) in the petri dish; the mould had lysed and killed the pathogen staphylococcus. The discovery of Penicillin is a fascinating story as it shows the dual role of serendipity and a prepared mind in its full glory. The mould Penicillium which secretes Penicillin grows best at 20°C, while for the pathogen staphylococcus the optimum temperature is 35°C. It is speculated that there must have been a snap cold during the intense summer of 1928 for the mould to grow and devour the pathogen. And the rest, as they say, is history.

The discovery of Penicillin that ushered in a newer line of treatment in the medicinal use of antibiotics in the 1950s had undoubtedly bestowed one of the greatest benefits to mankind. Over the following years, the average life span of the population increased significantly, as exemplified by Ms Anne Sheafe Miller, who, in 1942, was the first patient to be saved by Penicillin from a near-fatal streptococcal infection. She lived a full life, into her nineties, dying of natural causes in 1999. Newer antibiotics were discovered in rapid succession till the late sixties, so much so that the surgeon general of USA, Dr William Stewart, supposedly said to the US Congress, 'It is time for the United States to close the book on infectious disease.'

In retrospect, this statement has often been criticized in the light of the emergence of formidable infectious diseases, including AIDS, and the resurgence of older diseases in more virulent and antibiotic-resistant forms. Life has come a full circle; we may now be at the cusp of a 'pre-antibiotic era'. A recent study by the World Health Organization (WHO) indicates that the human and economic cost on account of antimicrobial resistance, if unchecked, would account for 10 million deaths a year globally and 2 per cent to 3.5 per cent less global GDP by 2050.

Bacteria resistant to front-line antibiotics are labelled as drug-resistant (DR), multi-drug resistant (MDR), or pan resistant (PR). The word 'superbug' is in general used for bacteria that are

MDR or PR in nature. Most of the infections caused by superbugs are picked up in a hospital environment, are extremely difficult to treat and have a high percentage of mortality. Nearly 30 per cent of all deaths in an ICU environment are caused by hard-to-treat or impossible-to-treat superbugs. The disease-setting is of an acute nature, meaning that the patient could be lost in forty-eight to seventy-two hours owing to septic shock.[8]

Unfortunately, India has the highest disease burden of hospital-acquired infections in the world. It is estimated that in the year 2015, India lost more than 2,50,000 adult patients to infection and about 60,000 babies to neo-natal infections. The numbers are only getting worse because of a combination of factors, including rampant abuse of antibiotics, exposure of bacteria to resistance development, lack of new antibiotics to deal with superbugs, and lack of investment in the infection area by global, big pharma companies. This is a problem that India needs to solve, and quickly!

Over the last four decades there has been no new class of antibiotics discovered specifically against one particular family of bacteria called the gram-negative bacteria. This family of bacteria has some of the most notorious members, such as *Acinetobacter*, *Pseudomonas*, *Klebsiella*, *E. coli*, and *Enterobacter*, which have collectively been deemed urgent and serious threats by WHO and Centre for Disease Control (CDC). The last-resort antibiotics in many cases is Colistin, a decades-old drug isolated from the bacteria *Paenibacillus polymyxa* that fell out of favour in human medicine due to its kidney toxicity. It remains one of the last-resort antibiotics for multidrug-resistant *Pseudomonas aeruginosa*, *Klebsiella pneumoniae*, and *Acinetobacter baumannii*. The rapidly increasing bacterial resistance to antibiotics is largely a result of the widespread and uncontrolled use of antibiotics. Until the mid '60s, everything seemed to be under control. In this period, new, natural sources of antibiotics like actinomycytes were identified and the number of new antibiotics, mainly analogs, increased almost exponentially. To eliminate antibiotic resistance, the pharmaceutical industry developed a new array of semi-synthetic antibiotics. After this 'golden age', from the late '60s onwards, the medical as well as economic climate changed, leading to a steep decline in antibiotics research even while the classical screening methods failed to identify new molecules. This has led to an environment favouring the onslaught of the so-called 'perfect storm' – no new antibiotics, a parallel rise in antimicrobial resistance, and diminished investments in antibiotics-discovery research.

*

Bugworks: AI to Antibiotics

The story of a company called Bugworks is exciting, since it has been trying to use artificial intelligence to simulate pre-clinical trials to hasten antibiotics discovery. Bugworks has been working on antibiotics discovery in an inventive manner, bringing together simulation models and ingenious microbiology techniques coupled with next-generational medicinal chemistry. This is the reason for the early successes of the company. Drug discovery is a long and complex process, with many failure trip points. Bugworks has produced anti-infective assets that are in the pre-clinical development phase; the company hopes to be able to convert some of these assets into lead compounds that will enter human clinical trials in a couple of years.

Next-generation medicinal chemistry is the key to higher-valued assets in the antibiotics class. There is a strong need to understand the action of the antibiotic at information levels deeper than what was explored in antibiotics in use over the last two to three decades. While ingenious experimental microbiology techniques provide a valuable tool to the medicinal chemist, the problem on hand is really one of multiple microbial variants that can potentially nullify the antibiotic effect, as historically observed in almost all classes of antibiotics in use.

Bugworks uses a computational platform where the network is built to copy the behaviour of the microbe, especially in infection related situations. Rather than time-consuming lab testing, the computational software replicates the effort put in the pre-clinical stage. This approach helps in cutting down the drug discovery cycle that traditionally extends to many decades of 'lab-experimentation'. The software acquires the genomic sequence information and offers enough analysis for the investigating chemist to arrive at relevant conclusions. This approach promises to cut the traditional drug discovery process by half.

The technology platform is modular and adaptable, to tackle a broad spectrum of pathogens that afflict large communities, hospitals and ICUs alike. The prowess of the platform lies in its ability to study interactions between segments in the physiology that are seemingly disconnected. This helps resurrect failing antibiotics, discover non-obvious combinations of synergistic drugs, and identify new mechanisms that are highly de-risked, hence increasing their probability of success.

The integrated platform tackles four major aspects that will lead to the next generation of successful antibiotic treatments. The first aspect deals with the problem of efflux. All gram-negative bacteria possess an array of pumps in their outer shell, which protect them from the continuous onslaught of 'foreign' substances in their natural milieu. Unfortunately, these pumps are the first line of defence that has to be breached in order for a drug to become an antibiotic. The platform delivers a stealth mode to the inhibitors, such that they become 'invisible' to the pumps. The second aspect of the platform deals with the ability to put forth effective combinations. The third aspect of the platform is its ability to model biofilms, which are robust bacterial populations that are resistant to conventional treatments, not by virtue of genetic mutations but because of their physical barriers. The fourth aspect of the platform deals with a unique computational approach to identify the target that is responsible for the antibacterial action of a given drug.

The second aspect of the integrated platform is best exemplified by the successful discovery of four-drug combinations for TB that are effective in late-stage animal models. This emerged from a very large search space of over a million combinations using the Bugworks' proprietary computational model of bacterial physiology. Using this platform technology, Bugworks has identified a 'potentiator chemical series' which renders drugs that were hitherto gram- negative ineffective to be highly effective. For example, the classes of drugs called macrolides are typically effective against gram positive bacteria and are rarely used to treat gram-negative infections. In combination with the potentiator lead, the macrolide classes of drugs are now very potent against gram-negative infections.

For the third aspect of the platform, Bugworks has developed an in-silico population model of biofilms. This model simulates the individual behaviour of about a million bacteria and predicts how individual bacteria respond to stress, whether it is antibiotics, nutritional, osmotic or pH. Bacterial survival strategies include the diversion of the system to biofilm formation and phenotypic drug resistance. Using the technology platform, Bugworks has an early pipeline of targets that are implicated in biofilm formation, that when inhibited will lead to the disruption of biofilms. The approach to tackling biofilms is holistic and comprehensive, thus creating a higher probability of delivering effective disruptors.

*

SigTuple: AI for Diagnostics

Another young company that is bringing a new technology approach to healthcare is SigTuple, whose co-founders had little or no experience in the medical sector. What they had was experience in building large-scale systems and research-focused tech teams.

SigTuple has been working on creating AI-based solutions for diagnostics and screening tests. This reduces the use of hardware and also provides results in a shorter time. It reads medical scans, images, and videos to help diagnose ailments.

The journey of SigTuple started in April 2015, when Rohit Kumar Pandey, Apurv Anand, and Tathagato Rao Dastidar were looking for an interesting and exciting problem for their venture to solve. They were looking for a problem that can positively impact the lives of billions. The healthcare industry caught their attention because of the enormous amount of data available and the potential of the insights that could be generated by churning that data. Although they didn't have any experience in the healthcare industry, they still decided to explore it because of the potential opportunity. The vision of the company was to revolutionize the global healthcare industry by developing smart screening solutions powered by artificial intelligence.

They downloaded a few publicly available datasets to come up with a demo to show how the AI worked. The demo was presented to some senior doctors in Bangalore for their feedback. The response to the demo was very motivating, and this led to the launch of SigTuple in July 2015.

SigTuple wanted to positively impact the masses with their solutions. Therefore, they decided to focus on the bottom-most layer of the healthcare diagnosis pyramid i.e. the common screening test. A significant number of common screening tests requires analysis of visual medical data, so the company decided to focus on peripheral blood smear analysis, urine and semen analysis, retinal and chest X-ray scan analysis.

Since the company wanted to develop solutions for multiple screening tests, SigTuple decided on a platform-centric approach i.e. a home-grown, continuous-learning AI platform to power multiple screening solutions. Additionally, this approach would help it to move from screening to diagnosis, prognosis, and future monitoring. SigTuple wanted to give an Indian flavour to the name of its platform and solutions. They named the AI platform, *Manthana*, coined from *samudra manthana*, the platform being a single unified one to churn the data and derive intelligence from it. The solution includes blood analysis, urine analysis, semen analysis, and retinal scan analysis.

When the company started working on an automated solution for peripheral blood smear analysis, it encountered the first bottleneck. It needed digital images to apply AI. However, the pathology industry was not completely digitized. The digitization solutions that existed were not scalable and were very expensive. This was one of the reasons why its competitors in the West started with radiology and ophthalmology first as those fields were already digitized. The promoters of SigTuple decided to take the bull by the horn and digitize pathology slides before applying AI.

Since this hardware/digital scanner was going to be enabled, they decided to take the standard microscope being used in a lab/hospital and transform it into a digital scanner.

Here is where the critical innovation specific to India occurred. They took a standard light microscope and added electromechanical components along with a cell phone to convert a microscope into a digital scanner. Now, with this hardware, a physical slide could be converted into a digital slide. This provided the solution they were looking for to get started with an AI-powered solution.

With the smart digital scanner in place, they could convert physical slides into digital data. Medical data is gold if it is annotated, so they had to get it annotated. They brought on board senior experts in the industry for the annotations and enhanced Manthana to support annotations.

The first prototypes of Shonit and Manthana were ready in February 2016, and the company was all set for the first clinical study. It took baby steps, starting the first study with normal samples. The results were very motivating, and it began looking for other screenings.

With some initial success with the first study, SigTuple started exploring more partnerships with hospitals and labs. SigTuple signed partnerships with multiple hospitals and labs to seek their support in developing its solutions.

SigTuple started working towards the regulatory and compliance requirements for its screening solutions and reached out to the Drug Controller General of India (DCGI). It completed the regulatory and compliance requirements, from an India perspective, by June 2016. It brought on board a regulatory and compliance expert dedicated to taking care of regulatory and compliance requirements at the company, not only for India but for other markets too.

Till April 2016, SigTuple was a six-member team. With work increasing significantly, it was decided to expand the team and add more members to the family. They added people who were smart, passionate, interested in applied research, and excited about the possibilities of AI in healthcare and medicine. The new hires included data scientists, platform development engineers, regulatory, and IP experts.

SigTuple is now working on setting up the manufacturing pipeline for pan-India distribution. Solutions for urine, semen, and retinal scans are in advanced stages of development, and the company plans to start the beta trail of these solutions by the first quarter of 2018. It is working to get regulatory clearances from other markets so that it can start expanding there by 2018.

*

There are many such stories playing out in the healthcare start-up ecosystem. Healthcare, almost always, has used the latest technology, but the issue of affordability remains. Hopefully the effort of large and small companies will ensure good results with improved affordability. For India, the real kranti will occur when technology-based start-ups and large healthcare organizations are able to improve inclusive healthcare for all Indians. This is a social need and perhaps a business case too.

At the annual meeting of the World Economic Forum in Davos in 2016, I attended one of the many exciting sessions on medical technology. 'Dreams are chemicals floating, reacting, together in the brain. Change some of the chemicals and you can change the dreams,' said one speaker. Memories are in the same league. They can be created or altered too. Bionic arms and limbs are a reality. Many ideas appear like science fiction today, but like the cyborg, they could soon be everyday matters.

7

HOSPITALITY AND TRAVEL

Technology for Quality at OYO

As a teenager, Ritesh Agarwal would often holiday with his parents. As a middle-class family living in a small town in Odisha, vacations meant visiting religious sites. Most middle-class families in India travel for broadly two reasons: weddings and events in the clan; or pilgrimage. Their travels are holiday, entertainment, school vacation, pilgrimage – all rolled into one. Young urban professionals may have the disposal income for weekend breaks and may travel purely for leisure, but for millions of Indian families, vacations mean trips to religious sites.

Ritesh and his family had two options for lodging. Either a relative's home, which meant cramped quarters, with two families squeezing into one house, or un-branded inns or hotels. There was almost no budget hotel that offered a uniformly clean experience.

'I was travelling continuously for three months searching for property after my twelfth grade, and during this time I realized that there was something wrong about each place; they were unpredictable and there was a surprise every time I checked in . . . In one place, the beds would be tall, in another, the washrooms were not clean. Yet another place didn't accept credit cards,' Ritesh remembers.

And this is where the idea of solving this problem came about – the offer of millions of rooms of un-branded hotels on a technology platform. Ritesh branded this offer OYO (On Your Own). An earlier version was called Oravle but it was renamed OYO.

By an estimate, there are 1.8 million un-branded hotel rooms in India, but barely 2 per cent can be reached online. Ritesh worked with his team to create a technology platform that could connect all these rooms across many hotels in thousands of cities and towns. Much like the travel sites Hotels.com and booking.com, OYO brought the same sophistication to a category of hotels that offered little more than a bed surrounded by four walls. Most of these rooms were dingy, unclean, and often unsafe. Hotel owners were more like landlords who rented the room by the night with not much investment in quality.

The only way to convince these hotels to be part of the OYO network was to ensure them higher returns and rates for their rooms; plus, the predictability of rentals. OYO created a platform that created as much trust among the hotel owners as among the potential travellers. While technology brought all the rooms under a common brand, a ground team of a few hundred people would visit every hotel, guiding each on how to upgrade its services. A checklist of thirty items was prepared to ensure consistency in quality standards across hotels and rooms.

The OYO ground team is connected to the main platform through their tablets as they visit and inspect hotels. The aim is to constantly monitor and assess adherence to the checklist for quality parameters.

OYO is also working to train professionals for the hotel sector. Hotel and hospitality management schools are not able to churn out enough professionals to cater to the demand, mostly because a large population of candidates, especially from small towns in India, can't afford the colleges.

'So imagine this, if someone wants to join the hospitality sector, he has to leave his home and go 300 km away for two years for training or college,' says Ritesh. To manage this, OYO has also launched a digital training programme for young candidates who want to work in the hotel and restaurant industry.

'The candidate can go just 500 metres away from his home and learn all this online from a computer. He can probably take his exam on his mobile phone and clear the first level in hospitality. Or probably take a break from his work for two hours and learn the course. That's a very big focus for us. We will build a fully democratic technology solution where anyone can work with us; this will ensure that quality of talent is retained and hospitality is seen as the choice of industry to work in, in the times to come. In the next three to five years, we are targeting more than 1,00,000 people through our initiatives. We believe this industry is growing at a ferocious pace.'

Training in technology will also create a cadre of professionals that is ready to accept new ways of delivering old services. The technology being deployed by OYO is not just the web-based platform. It also removes many functions and creates others. Most of its customers use OYO's system for automated and web check-in. With this option, the front-desk team in all hotels can be reduced and redeployed.

'In reality, we can't run away from the technological revolution. Remember, there will soon come a time when we won't need humans during the time of check-in, it will be fully automated. But when people are replaced with technology, it isn't a zero-sum game. Hotels have been struggling for a very long time to build a great culture inside their accommodation. We are investing heavily in front-office people who can be great community managers too and not restrict themselves to their daily mundane jobs,' says Ritesh.

This means that hotel professionals who are manning the front desk can be redeployed for other functions in customer care.

*

Lalit and Taj Hotels: Hospitable Technology

The existing hotels chains that offer about 1,12,000 branded rooms are also rapidly finding themselves in the same situation. Chains like Lalit and Taj are increasingly leaning on technology for many functions. The objective is the same: to automate repetitive tasks and re-task the professionals for problem-solving and consumer-connect functions.

The hospitality industry has certainly come a long way since the first inn welcomed its first guest. But much of the transformation has happened in the last few centuries. The invention of engines meant man could travel faster and wider than ever before, and as costs went down, the number of travellers – on business or for pleasure – rose. But it really wasn't until the true pioneers of modern hospitality saw the benefits of economies of scale that the industry really changed.

One of the earliest hotel chains in the world, if not the oldest, is the Kempinski, founded in 1897. The Taj group opened its first hotel, the Indian flag-bearer to this day, in Mumbai in 1903. The Hilton and the Marriot started their respective businesses in 1919 and 1927, but were among the first of their kind to operate in multiple locations, offering the same kind of experience to their discerning clientele. Motel 6 in the United States, which offered more affordable rooms to the less affluent, started its operations in 1962.

A quick look at the timeline tells you that it's in the past fifty years that the industry has become more organized. As flights and telephones connected more and more parts of the world, the ambitious groups (some of whom are mentioned above) started to expand their operations organically and inorganically through construction, franchising, and acquisition.

It wasn't just the boarding business that underwent this change. Following the war and global acceptance of America's 'coolness', the post-war years – until America's sheen wore off with the Vietnam war, among other misadventures – saw their home-grown businesses, such as Coca Cola, PepsiCo, and Kentucky Fried Chicken, become popular names in other parts of the world. Franchising was a key element of their business model, for it allowed them to get past the protectionist policies in many of the markets they entered.

Yet, for all the change that was happening in the world of hospitality, the industry was never ambitious about technology the way finance or medicine was. Innovations were mainly on the client-facing side: televisions, cable programmes, hot water, etc. In the recent years, however, technology has played a remarkable role in transforming the industry on both fronts – the client side as well as the operational side.

Spending on the client side includes platforms that allow guests to book through a variety of means. The means have made matters infinitely simpler for the discerning traveller. Rating engines help him arriving at a yes/no decision, offering the best of available information. Other investments include end-to-end systems, such as apps or internal data systems that remember guest preferences, dietary restrictions, correlate purchases and create avenues for up-/cross-selling, add-ons like Wi-Fi or local conveyance, automatic air-conditioning, sensor-based lighting, etc. The idea these days is to create a home-away-from-home for the leisure traveller, and a business-centre-wherever-you-are for business travellers.

On the service side, the effort has been on several fronts.

Resource usage – using analytics to identify peak and weak times for resource demand – enables businesses to hire according to forecast instead of committing resources the year round. The business intelligence gathered includes what a customer/group will expect or demand, what is available, what needs to be sourced, etc. Additionally, hotels can sublet space to other commercial interests – such as a boutique or entertainment store – based on what businesses guests are most likely to patronize during their stay. The new tools also track who's bringing in referrals, who will be price conscious about rooms but will pay for additional services, guests who have a history of destructive behaviour, lifetime values, etc. The next step, naturally, is the setting up of loyalty programmes for desirable guests. The casinos of Las Vegas and other, similar hotspots across the world, already 'comp' their high-rollers for rooms, calculating that their spending on the premises will more than make up for the discounts they offer.

Hotels are also experimenting with digital concierges and self-check-in kiosks that reduce manpower requirements, thereby bringing down costs too. For the hotel chains, even repeatability – or the standardization of experiences at all their different outlets – is a major must-have. A unified platform is but the first step towards such a direction.

Importantly, these technical systems cut off reliance on personnel's personal connection to guests. When an employee leaves, he takes his accumulated information and learning with him; now the machine learns, and the company doesn't lose out on this knowledge for perpetuity.

Rakesh Sarna, the former CEO of Indian Hotels Company that runs the Tata-owned Taj Hotels chain, is pragmatic about the growing impact of technology on the sector. In a conversation with me, he recognized the important role technology is playing in the industry. He was also candid enough to say that some jobs will be lost.

'An aspect of technology changes that needs to be kept in mind is that it is going to replace a significant portion of manual jobs. For instance, there is a growing shift to a cooking method called sous vide, wherein the food is cooked in airtight plastic bags, and this has made cooking quicker, tastier, and easier to sustain at room temperatures. So earlier, there used to be 100 chefs serving a banquet of 300 people trying to prepare all the food, but now the work can be done by just five,' Sarna says.

He feels that instead of being despondent about the changes, the industry must work on empowering their teams with better abilities, 'One of the biggest challenges in skilling and reskilling will be to keep up with the technology changes. If we take the specific example of hospitality sector, it is largely driven by customer/guest behaviour, and the guest's needs and desires are changing rapidly, largely due to the technological advances. Digital literacy is the biggest task at hand because even a housekeeping cleaner would need to learn how to use digital technology to be able to do his or her job. The nature of jobs in hospitality and related services sector will change, and with that a change in the required skill-set will become mandatory.'

Jyotsna Suri, chairperson and managing director of Bharat Hotels that run the Lalit Group of hotels, holds a similar view: 'The hospitality industry in India has also evolved manifold over the years. With technology growing at jet speed in India, the obvious effects have also manifested in this sector. Interestingly, this has not necessarily made a huge dent in employment opportunities. The purpose is to leverage technology to improve and to reduce costs, improve efficiency and improve productivity without undermining people. For instance, the use of solar energy has significantly reduced costs. The use of information technology has helped to streamline information under different modules for booking, for instance.'

She cites an interesting way in which hotels are changing. 'Today an F&B manager has his own internal set up where he knows exactly what the recipe of a particular dish is. Integration of inventory management with IT has helped operations and day-to-day functioning, and we don't have to keep records.

Technology has helped operations immensely, for instance, in the case of corporate buying for hotels, and you can know very quickly which hotel has how many bed sheets and pillow cases, etc. Hence, in terms of synergies, technology has significantly helped. For example, with the help of technology, obtaining daily critical information about my group, such as its total revenues, is just an SMS away. This results in saving time that would be earlier wasted on collation and manpower. Now you have the system in place giving details of what exactly is happening. You know in a minute where you are going.'

Such efficiencies are important for hotel operations, where every room is a perishable product. If it is not sold, there is loss of revenue.

*

MakeMyTrip's Online Journey

The travel and hospitality sector will continue to grow and contribute to the economy. According to an India Brand Equity Foundation (IBEF) report, it is about 7.5 per cent of India's GDP, contributing $46 billion USD (3x of 2006) to the Indian economy, and is growing at a rate of nearly 5 per cent.[1]

Hotels are expected to employ almost 15 million people in 2016–17. Despite an apparent economic slowdown, hotel bookings have doubled and international tourists to India have increased by 196 per cent. Not surprising then that national and international chains are investing heavily in expansion both in the business and tourism segments in India. But the current surge is being driven by business travellers.

Occupancy rates in India, at 60.3 per cent, are higher than in Europe or the Middle East. At the same time, revenue per available room (RevPAR) is lower due to the price-conscious culture in India and high expectations on the service front even from budget hotels. Demand has increased at 11–12 per cent per annum, but availability has not kept pace, growing at 5 per cent only.

The travel industry took off with the rise of booking sites like MakeMyTrip (MMT). The concept of booking travel and hotels through a website was a radical idea when it began with the start of the new millennium in the year 2000.

MakeMyTrip was founded on 1 April 2000. Created to empower the Indian traveller with instant booking and comprehensive choices, the company began its journey in the US–India travel market. It aimed to offer a range of best-value products and services, along with cutting-edge technology and dedicated round-the-clock customer support.

In many ways, the story of MMT is also the story of how the industry started to use technology for travel-related activities. Hotels, airlines, and the railways industry worked together to ensure that consumers could get rapid solutions to their travel needs.

Post the dotcom crash and 9/11, there was virtually no appetite for a business-to-consumer (B2C) Internet play, that too in travel. The choice for the promoters of MakeMyTrip was to either wind down and go back to the corporate world or to somehow muster further investment. Internet penetration in India stood at a mere 0.5 per cent in 2000, growing to about 2 per cent by 2004.

'When we started out, we raised money fairly quickly – from eVentures, one of the first venture capital firms of the time. Both the euphoria and funding were short-lived, as we soon found ourselves in the middle of the dotcom bust. The second promised tranche did not come through as our fund shut shop. We invested all of our personal savings, took money from angel investors, right-sized the business and focused on turning profitable. This helped us run a tight ship. We worked on a bootstrap model for the next eighteen months, and turned profitable in 2003,' says Rajesh Magow, co-founder of MMT.

'Two key occurrences in the external environment led us to believe that the Indian market is finally ready to open up for online travel bookings. The IRCTC website was launched in 2002, and India's first-ever low-cost carrier, Air Deccan, was launched in 2003. The first is significant as it was the first catalyst driving consumers to shift from offline to online booking of tickets for their primary mode of travel back then – rail. The second is significant as the emergence of low-cost carriers implied that air travel would now become affordable,' Magow explains.

Internet penetration in India stood at 2.4 per cent then, and would grow to 5.1 per cent by 2009. Indigo Airlines was launched in 2006. It was also around this time that air e-ticketing finally took off in India.

'We decided to invest in opening up destinations for leisure travel in India, and in an effort to do so, we launched our first charter flight to Leh in 2010. We also started investing in our customer support during this period,' says Magow.

When MMT launched in India in 2000, its first user interface was built on the Dot Net platform by an outsourced company. The earliest rendition of the site was highly unstable, in fact the website crashed during the launch press conference. Higher-than-expected incoming traffic was one of the underlying reasons for the crash. To counter this, MMT added more hardware. Often when the site crashed, users could see the 'under maintenance' message on the site.

The majority of the bookings which were confirmed at the front-end, failed at the back-end. Many airlines did not even have APIs. MMT was screen-scraping them back then. Screen-scraping, at the time, involved reading the details on an agent's screen and then manually acting on it. Interestingly, while users could book online, the operations team was unable to process the bookings. MMT realized it had forgotten to create an admin panel for this. The panel was created overnight.

This was still the era of paper tickets. There were special printers for printing out airline tickets. The typical booking cycle was this: the customer books the ticket online, MMT processes the booking at their end, prints out the tickets, and has them couriered to the customer. This meant one could not book through MMT for urgent, last-minute travel. During this time, MMT was doing about 400 transactions per day and shipping out seven to eight cartons of tickets. Given that its systems could not handle the load, the processing was tedious and time-consuming.

Mid-2006, MMT tried automating the printing process. This backfired as the printer was unable to handle fast processing. MMT had to deploy people whose only task was to ensure printing of tickets in a manner that the printer did not get stuck.

The team also started working on building MMT 2.0. They again relied on an external party to build it. They took the decision of building MMT 2.0 on Java stack instead of on Dot Net and hired the services of Nurun, a Canada-based company, for its visual design requirements.

Between 2007 and 2010, the company worked hard to make its systems more robust. MMT 2.0 was launched, but it too crashed. It took a couple of months to stabilize systems. It was during this time that MMT decided to invest in building its own in-house technology team. This was a challenge as talent with requisite experience and expertise was scarce. MMT ended up hiring people with experience in software solutions companies and training them for its internal requirements. While the business was growing, the foundation was not that of a technology-focused company; there were no code development disciplines, and therefore there were plenty of scalability problems. All these issues had to be addressed ground up.

In 2010, MakeMyTrip had a blockbuster IPO on NASDAQ and was among the first Internet companies in India to list in the US. MMT had now become a household name for booking air tickets online. At this time, the majority of its revenues was coming from its air business.

From 2010 to 2013, it was a time of relative stability. Internet penetration had started growing rapidly in India. Broadband connectivity was finally coming of age. The penetration stood at 7.5 per cent in 2010, and would double by 2013.

At MakeMyTrip, the air business was growing and the company started investing in the hotels business now. MMT acquired Hoteltravel.com in 2012 as a measure to fuel its hotels business growth.

MMT also launched many customer-centric features riding on technology. MMT tried experimenting with value-additions to customer interactions by launching apps such as MyTripIdeas, TripAlong, and RoutePlanner, the last one being an app that makes travel planning faster and easier. RoutePlanner integrates availability of services like flights, buses, trains, and cabs to display all possible connectivity options between destinations in India. The company was continuously finding ways to value-add to the traveller's experience, in the wake of growing competition.

By this time, MakeMyTrip had emerged as the dominant market leader in the online travel space. Phocuswright in its 2013 report said the company had a whopping 47 per cent market share, the highest among all online travel agents in the country.

Mobile was beginning to pick up speed in India, and in order to tap into this, MMT launched its first Responsive and Adaptive Webpage in 2012–13.

The era of smartphones began in 2014, and again changed the entire industry. Increasing disposable income and availability of affordable smartphones paved the way for the mobile ecosystem in India. Owing to this, the Internet penetration grew from 15 per cent in 2013 to an estimated 34 per cent in 2016. MMT started making organic and inorganic investments to boost the travel ecosystem. These investments included easytobook.com, Simplotel, and Holiday IQ.

In July 2015, MMT invested US $5 million in Bona Vita Technologies. 'The company is building what we believe will disrupt the holiday packages segment in the future,' Magow says.

Realizing that the next wave of growth will be driven by mobile customers, MMT has been focusing on strengthening and bringing customer-centricity to its mobile platforms. 'In early 2015, we stopped all work on other technology aspects for nearly three months and focused entirely on creating and building a future-growth-ready mobile app. Today, MakeMyTrip has been rated as one of the best travel apps for consumers in India. Our efforts have yielded phenomenal results. Of the over 23 million app downloads we have registered, 8 million have happened in the last six months. Over 70 per cent of our domestic hotel transactions came via mobile in Q1 FY2017. We also conducted the first-ever app-only travel sale – the Great Indian Getaway – in October 2015. It was a phenomenally successful sale that helped us gain 1 million app downloads during the sale-window period,' says Magow.

Leading with Technology – Mobile and Big Data

The pace of change in technology over the last few years has been mind-boggling. The travel segment lends itself naturally to a more enriched mobile experience – after all, travel has everything to do with mobility and 'being on the move'. Big data is an enabler of endless possibilities, ranging from customer segmentation and targeting, to providing enriched and personalized experiences leading to customer delight.

On the consumption side, mobile has changed the way consumers interact with MMT's services. On the back-end processing side, there's a lot more data that MMT now captures and processes. The combination of the two, however, offers its own set of challenges, as well as opportunities. 'There's so much data and so little screen space. And we have choppy networks and limited device capabilities! What do you show and what do you hide? How often do you capture customer data? How often do you provide personalized assistance to your valuable customers? Too much interaction, and you start appearing to be intrusive and nagging. Too little interaction, and you lose engaging the customer. Striking a balance is necessary.'

In the sections below are some examples of how MMT uses the combination of big data and mobile to provide better, enriched experience to its customers. Before we get into examples, Magow helps me understand the context of big data and mobile in the travel segment, and their nuances in India:

Customer insight: Like all consumer-Internet businesses, we capture the click-stream of users when they are on our site. This data is used within the session to enrich the user-experience, and also in offline, batch-processing mode to gain better insight into the business, and to deepen our understanding of our customers' preferences and behaviours. We also capture the customer's preferred platform of engagement – whether the customer is accessing our services via the desktop or a mobile device. If the customer is on the mobile device, we would like to understand the specifics of the device – its capabilities, network type and network speed, operating systems (iOS or Android), etc.

Supplier and Partner ecosystem insight: MMT works with a multitude of suppliers – airlines, airline global distribution systems (GDS)/aggregation systems, hotels, hotel GDS/ aggregators, package providers, bus/rail/cab suppliers, etc. Over a period of time, one gets familiar with the pattern of interaction with any supplier. We use big data to glean insights from our supplier network to understand our pattern of interaction with the suppliers, such as, who do we do more business with, where do we make more profits from, and above all, who provides the best experience to our valued customers. On the partner ecosystem front, we work with payment gateways, banks, and several service and technology providers. A good understanding of what works and what doesn't work within this ecosystem is critical for us to provide the best experience to our customers.

The idiosyncrasies of mobile technologies in India: There is great variability in the mobile experience in India. The network connections are choppy, and vary widely across 2G, 3G, 4G, and Wi-Fi networks. The device types are also quite an eclectic mix, ranging from high-end, sophisticated phones to the cheapest low-end phones with very little memory and processing power. Typically, the lower-end phones are coupled with poorer network connectivity too, and this makes it extremely challenging to provide the users any semblance of a rich user experience. Towards this, MMT has done some serious work on providing a great experience to its customers even on low-end devices and in poor network conditions. MMT has recently launched a dedicated product line to cater to this segment – the web app would now replace its mobile and desktop sites. This progressive web app will be both network- and device-capability-aware, and would adjust to variability both on the network side as well as on the device-capability side.

Here are some examples below of how MakeMyTrip uses big data and mobile technologies to drive customer delight and to lay the foundations of a sound, profitable business.

Hotel reviews: Take the example of a customer who is looking to book a hotel. Before zeroing in on and paying for a hotel, most customers want to see how other users have rated the hotel and what kind of reviews they have written for the hotel. If one had the time and a big enough screen, it would be easy to read all reviews and get a better sense of the hotel. However, in reality, one has neither the time nor the inclination to read extensively – on a mobile screen especially. To assist the user better, it's best to give him a summary of all the reviews in a bite-sized consumable chunk. MMT uses machine learning to construct a summary of all reviews that are available for the hotel and offers it to the user so that he/she can find the information in an easy-to-consume fashion, thus assisting him/her with the hotel purchase.

Marketing-spend optimization: MMT uses various paid marketing channels to promote their hotels to different types of customers. In a paid marketing medium, MMT pays the cost of the click upfront, with no guarantee that the click will lead to a purchase by the user. MMT uses historical data, seasonality, and price competitiveness to identify the hotel/check-in date combinations that will lead to the highest return on investment (ROI) for the marketing spend.

Some use-cases driven by user-segmentation and personalization: MMT employs big data analytics to gain a better understanding of its customers. Like other eCommerce companies, MMT does customer segmentation that can be used further for customer targeting and personalization. Some of the considerations that go into segmentation are: (i) past buying behaviour of users, (ii) recent search history of users, (iii) number of travellers and their age-profiles, (iv) device characteristics of these users, like the specifics of their desktop browser and mobile capabilities, etc. Some use-cases within the travel space are as follows:

Hotel listing order: When a customer is looking for a hotel, MMT serves out a list of hotels from which the customer can select the one that best suits her needs. This list is personalized for the user, depending on which segment MMT has mapped the user into.

Cross-sell, persuasion, and recommendation: As a simple, straightforward example, for every flight user who is not buying a hotel from MMT, it makes sense to recommend a set of hotels to the customer in the destination city. MMT reaches out to customers on several channels: email, SMS, and mobile app notifications.

Hotel content normalization: The most important inputs a customer uses to make a decision to purchase a hotel are its description, facilities, room details, and images. In order to help the customer make the right decision, MMT collects this content from multiple sources to provide a rich experience to her. However, collecting this content from multiple sources has two core issues – duplication of items (e.g., image of a hotel lobby may be collected from the hotel website as well as from a third party paid vendor), and redundancy of content (descriptions like *swimming pool* and *outdoor swimming pool* may be received from different sources for the same hotel).

MMT employs sophisticated machine learning algorithms to identify similar text and images, and present the most optimized content to its users.

*

Automation and data analytics will make the travel experience smoother. Unlike in other segments, this sector will still need human interaction, so jobs will remain. However, the nature of work will evolve rapidly. The Indian government's efforts to arrange for electronic visas is taking root and will become more efficient with time. Travel regulators are already running pilot projects for paper-free boarding of flights. For the travel companies and policy makers, the big effort should be on data analytics. With millions of Indians ready to join the travelling middle class, understanding these patterns could unveil new directions for growth.

8

BANKING AND FINANCE

It was the late 1990s. HDFC Bank had been given a licence to start operations about four years ago. A private housing finance company had been given a license to launch a bank! This was a novelty for generations of Indians who didn't even consider the possibility of a private bank. The only private banks were a clutch of MNCs like CitiBank that catered to the very affluent.

When HDFC Bank opened its branch in New Delhi's Vasant Vihar area, its CEO, Aditya Puri, spoke a language that few understood. 'Our bank will run on a technology platform. Customers will be able to get information and transact without having to visit the branch,' he told me at the inauguration of the branch.

HDFC introduced a single account number for each customer so that the customer could transact at any branch of the bank. The bank had built a connected network that allowed the customer to access any branch in its rapidly expanding countrywide network. The ATMs ensured that people didn't have to queue up with slips for withdrawing money from surly tellers.

This was a disruptive effort at a time when personal computers were still a rare sight at nationalized banks. Even when there were computers at a bank, they were often not connected to each other even within the branch, let alone between branches. A customer could only transact at the branch where his or her account had been created. Any other branch of the same bank would treat the customer as a stranger.

Perhaps no other industry has been as open to the adoption of technology as banking and finance. From the earliest days of its existence, when money was converted into 'chits' that could then be converted back into useful currency in a distant town, financiers have always been at the forefront of the quest for easier, faster ways to handle money.

Some of the earliest institutions were lending organizations – either cooperatives or the fiefdoms of rich, private families. Over a period of time, these enterprises started to consolidate through mergers or buyouts. The combined entities then leveraged their bigger sizes to both offset the risk of collapse and service customers who needed more funds. Over a period of time, the 'chits' of the old civilizations turned into 'letters of introduction' from one banker to another in a faraway land, vouching for the bearer and honoured in the best traditions of *quid pro quo.*

The emergence of unified currencies across nations or administrations – the dollar in the USA, the English pound-sterling across the British Empire, the mark in the German colonies – replacing the traditional metal-based coinages, and the acceptance of the gold standard, made things simultaneously simpler and more difficult. For while there were fewer calculations to be made during conversion, there were also, suddenly, so many more things you could do with such funds. The barter system went out the window – now you could exchange what you had for currency instead of having to settle for whatever goods the other side could offer. It opened up the world of speculation and trading to the financier, a world where the possibilities were many magnitudes greater than ever before.

Most of these changes have happened in the last three centuries, many within the last century itself. Small, parochial banks existed, but in pockets; their turfs were quickly taken over by bigger financial institutions that had both muscle and reach. While the old understandings were still honoured, the new banks were more aggressive in their outlook. Their war-chests grew to match the treasuries of small nations.

With the emergence of new technologies like the telegraph, steam-propelled engines and, later, the telephone, these institutions could now spread their nodes, their branches, across the world. Information could be sent and received almost overnight, a dramatic change from when the speed of a message depended on the couriers and horses the sender could afford. Newly-minted accountants and managers were dispatched to distant branches and tasked with keeping the books in shape.

But the explosive growth also brought with it explosive headaches. Different banks had different systems for tracking the money entrusted to/by them. The simple act of reconciliation between three different branches could be an onerous process, despite the replacement of traditional computing tools such as the abacus with, what was for that time cutting-edge technology, the adding machines. The increase in size had not been matched by a corresponding increase in capability.

Until, in 1950, the Bank of America (BoA) decided that the status quo was not acceptable any longer. Roping in Stanford Research Institute (now known as SRI International), BoA wanted to find a way to process cheques faster. Not only did SRI eventually come up with a working prototype of the Electronic Recording Machine, Accounting (ERMA), but it also suggested operational changes such as indexing accounts by number instead of by name and using the Magnetic-Ink Character Reader to scan cheques for identification – solutions that have survived the test of time so far.

Soon, other banks that could afford it, invested in a similar technology. As computing power increased, technology began to play a bigger role. Ledgers became electronic; computers were used, first for complicated calculations, then for storage, retrieval, and processing. Soon, even though the credit for its invention is still disputed, the ATM made its arrival . . . and the world of banking would never be the same again.

The leaps in computing power and the advancement in microchips led to the introduction of terminals that were connected to a large, central processing unit (usually a mainframe system), but could be used by authorized employees to enter transactions, check balances, and run credit reports, flag accounts, etc.

The cost of connecting various branches was prohibitively expensive at first, and it was only the large banks – which could effect economy of scale in their operations – that went for large-scale computerization. Even the ATMs, still a novelty in the late 1980s for much of the bank-serviced crowd, had to be located within or near a branch so that they could be connected to the network. It wasn't until the emergence of the Internet and, later, the protocols to ensure secured communications between two parties, that computerization became the must-have transition instead of simply a good-to-have option.

The innovations weren't restricted to banking alone. Stock exchanges around the world moved from traditional outcry systems to electronic order matching. An interesting bit of trivia here: it wasn't the famous New York Stock Exchange that pioneered this, but the lesser-known Mid-West Stock Exchange, now called the Chicago Stock Exchange. It wasn't too long before traders could place their orders from dedicated terminals within their respective stock exchanges and get them executed immediately, cutting down last-minute risks.

Financial technology, or fintech as we commonly refer to it, was finally born! Let's take a quick look at some of the elements that fintech refers to.

Fintech refers to the industry – it is no longer just a sub-industry – that offers technology-enabled solutions in the financial sector. Fintech includes data-centres and crypto-currencies (a purely-digital currency, such as bitcoin, litecoin, namecoin, etc., that may not be controlled by the central bank of any particular nation) and everything in between. Although the term has been around for a while – indeed, it might very well have originated with the ERMA itself – it is only in the past fifty years that it has come to be seen as an industry in its own right.

The pace of innovation has picked up again of late, with banks across the world once again opening up their purses for upgrades and outright transformations. While they are still conservative, in that they would rather opt for a safe solution already backed by some other bank, the constant encroachment on their turf by new-gen banks – which stress on technology to sell and deliver products, and hype the conveniences such an approach offers – may soon force them to take a more proactive approach in adopting disruptive technologies.

Most of the innovations appear to be in the front-end of the business, consisting of newer ways of reaching out and staying in touch with customers, recording their experiences during transactions, location- or profile-based communications – for instance, a young couple entering a bank might suddenly receive an invitation to talk to an officer about a housing loan at rates affordable to them, or a young professional may be directed to the vehicle loans desk after he/she pauses at a poster of a BMW – managing the diverse needs of a diverse clientele, or offering competitive rates and benefits while keeping costs in control. To keep costs in control, branches are being downsized, and traditional tasks such as those related to deposits, withdrawals, and statements are being automated. A MarketsandMarkets study estimates that expenditure on customer experience is growing at a rate of 21.1 per cent and will hit about 13 billion dollars in 2021.[1]

With reduced footprints on the ground, banks will place a greater responsibility on their call centres to address queries from customers. Since most of the banks already outsource this function, the onus of upgrading their infrastructure and managing adherence of their operatives will remain on the vendors, and will not require a disproportional increase in investment from the banks.

Many financial institutions are also exploring ways to make their back-end systems, transactional and analytical, better.

Legacy systems are no longer the only solutions for complicated, large-scale applications; cloud computing, blockchains, and distributed processing have brought about a paradigm shift in how organizations can operate millions of data points. While some banks, such as ANZ, maintain that their existing systems are sufficient, others – such as the Commonwealth Bank of Australia and Nationwide in the UK – recently completed multi-billion dollar upgrades to their core banking systems.

Data analytics is being used by financial institutions (FIs) – banking and otherwise – to identify correlations that can help predict bad debts, possible non-performing assets, insider trading, terror funding, money laundering, etc. However, with firms both big and small vying for valuable contracts in the analytics space, which is itself still evolving, companies are having a tough time choosing between cost and guaranteed benefits.

Another innovation that is still in its infancy is branchless banking – banks operating purely in the digital space, customers serviced by apps or websites, and having only an unseen customer service centre to approach with queries. Given the loss of faith in the banking system since the crisis in 2008 and people's traditional faith in a brick-and-mortar establishment, these digital banks haven't cut the umbilical cord from their parent organizations and it remains to be seen whether they will ever be able to do so.

For much of the past decade, India lagged behind the more developed economies in terms of its banking infrastructure, banking reach, and application of technology by banks. The nationalization of banks in 1969 and then later in 1980 meant that they did not have to compete aggressively in order to survive; as government entities, they were now secured from collapse, their employees protected from punitive action for non-performance of duties. The presence of international banks like Citibank, BNP Paribas, and JP Morgan did not affect them because these banks catered to the high-value customers while the bottom of the pyramid was still beholden to the home-grown ones. It wasn't until local private banks such as HDFC and ICICI entered the scene that the situation improved.

HDFC Bank was the first to bring ATMs to the Indian customer in 1998. It was an innovation that dramatically altered the expectations Indians had from banks. Protectionist policies in many places delayed the large-scale adoption of ATMs, for fear that computerization and teller machines would put loyal employees out of work. It was only after a generous Voluntary Retirement Scheme package was rolled out across the country that the objections were muted. However, the lack of communication and power infrastructure to support the installation of ATMs meant that it would still be a while before every citizen with a bank account could use one.

But since then, perhaps recognizing the necessity of evolving to ensure survival, banks in India have been enthusiastic about adopting technology to augment their operations. In the past few decades, driven by the RBI and stakeholders like CII, every commercial bank in India has adopted a core banking system that enables National Electronics Fund Transfer (NEFT), Real-time Gross Settlement (RTGS), and Immediate Payment Service (IMPS) transactions across the board. According to an RBI report of August 2016, there are over 2 lakh ATMs and close to 15 lakh POS terminals in the country (excluding ATMs and POSes outside the RBI ambit, such as those of cooperative banks). And while there is still a lot of human intervention at the services level, such as for approving loans or overdrafts, banks are exploring ways to make services more machine-driven.

The major stock exchanges of India have also gone electronic, performing at par with the best in the world. Portfolios, whether they are of the stock market or investment instruments like insurance or loans, have mostly been dematerialized. When the government announced the institution of a biometric-protected digital locker to save all essential records, the banks quickly embraced the idea and offered free facilities for its customers.

Insurance companies allow premiums to be paid online. However, their agents are still the primary sales drivers and the go-to resources when customers seek clarity about the terms and conditions of a policy.

Another innovation, although not unique to India, is the permitting of algorithmic trading. However, the Securities and Exchanges Board of India (SEBI) is mulling changes to the trading system so as to eliminate any unfair advantages a co-located trader would have over a remote one, since even a microsecond's advantage (on account of geographical proximity to the stock exchange's data centre) can be the difference between profit and loss.

For the last few years, Indian institutions have been focusing on bringing financial access to about 800 million who remain on the margin. Much of the attempt has been to ensure that banks, micro-finance institutions, and other related bodies reach individuals in remote parts of the country.

The effort then moved to ensuring that even the urban poor have bank accounts. The policy makers realized that distance from a bank branch was not the problem. It was the access to a bank that was. A migrant to a city could be a few feet away from a bank branch but still be unable to open an account. Innovative methods of using banking correspondents and mobile-based account management were deployed. As a result, while millions more accounts were created, most remained dormant. The account holders did not know how to manage their accounts. They still did not have the ability to transact.

The policy makers went back to work and chose to come up with a solution based on the Aadhaar identification card. This has allowed migrants and those in remote areas to be better known by the banking system. The banks can now depend on an identity that could allow them to know their new-found customers better.

The Aadhaar project, once billed as a game-changer for social security in India, finally started living up to its billing in the past few years when the NDA government, taking over the reins from the UPA, decided to reinvigorate it instead of consigning it to history as a poorly-executed project. One of the first measures of the NDA government was to link LPG (domestic gas which is used for cooking and is heavily subsidized by the central government) subsidies to Aadhaar identities. Where middlemen used to profit off these subsidized cylinders by selling them to commercial users and pocketing the difference, now the rebate was credited directly into the bank accounts of the original owners. There is no longer an incentive for commercial users to buy on the black market since the prices are all the same now.

That, in a manner of speaking, was only the first shot across the bow from Aadhaar's quiver. Since then, even as a massive database clean-up has been taking place, Aadhaar has been made mandatory for opening bank accounts, buying SIM cards, etc. During the Jan Dhan Yojana scheme, lakhs and lakhs of people were encouraged to open bank accounts, requiring only the Aadhaar card to satisfy Know Your Customer (KYC) norms. It is now easy for the government to link bank accounts to specific individuals through the Aadhaar card. This was unimaginable earlier because the proofs used (passport, PAN card, DL, etc.) were not connected to each other, and could therefore not be used to pinpoint common ownership.

To ensure that Aadhaar itself is not misused, any transaction using the system requires biometric and OTP authentication. While this places a bigger load on the technical infrastructure, it makes opening a bank account in Aadhaar-enabled branches a quick and breezy process.

The recent demonetization decision by the Government of India has given a fillip to financial inclusivity by forcing people to deposit high-denomination notes in banks instead of using them as legal tender. It also forced people to use their bank accounts more frequently. Subsequently, there has been a genuine uptake in electronic transactions. E-wallets have cashed in, as have banks and new-gen digital payment banks such as Airtel and Jio. PayTM has reported over 50 lakh transactions in a forty-five-day period since demonetization, although it must also be added that this claim has not been verified independently. The Unified Payment Interface and the Rupay card – both initiatives of the National Payments Corporation of India – are yet to find mass-scale traction, but there is no doubt about the government's enthusiasm for these solutions.

In 2016, the government also introduced a mobile app, BHIM (Bharat Interface for Money) that would act as a single-stop shop for banking transactions by connecting accounts to mobile numbers. This simplifies the process of e-transfers, since it is no longer necessary to remember long bank account numbers. You can transfer funds to someone else through the app as long as you know their mobile number.

With a young population quite at ease with smartphones and technology, the time is ripe for embracing a technology regime in the financial sector in the country. Providing e-banks might prove easier than creating brick-and-mortar outlets in remote areas, and banks certainly seem to be leaning in that direction. The launch of payment banks, which use the Aadhaar system for authentication and operate out of your neighbourhood *kiranas* and pop-up shops, may prove that banks can run without dedicated branches and personnel.

Even as this Aadhaar-based system is rolling out, a new concept is taking root in the financial ecosystem. The financial services industry is realizing that it is not enough to just enhance inclusion. Creating customers is not as important as converting them into credit-worthy consumers.

Creating Borrowers with Suvidhaa

Banks don't need just depositors, they need credit-worthy borrowers. A million new depositors are not necessarily credit-worthy borrowers. The solution then is to create millions of new borrowers and not just account holders. Lending now leans on technology to ensure that the credit profile of the least likely borrowers is made bankable. Certain business models make sense only when they are flipped around. And these strategies succeed only when they are seen from every angle possible.

A few pioneers have embarked on this path already. Payment and remittance company Suvidhaa Infoserve has evolved a unique process of managing remittances. This process allows a user to have a credit profile. Using a proprietary technology platform, Suvidhaa closely tracks the domestic remittances made by its customers. Customers deposit small sums of cash at Suvidhaa counters and have the satisfaction of the money reaching their hometown within hours. Each of these transactions adds to the credit profile of the depositor. Suvidhaa has now launched the Nano credit scheme in association with Axis Bank, allowing its customers to borrow sums ranging from ₹10,000 to ₹25,000 with no extra paperwork. These consumers need to quote only the customer identity used for remittances. 'We run this system based on trust, which is based on the customer's track record. And it has worked wonderfully so far,' says Paresh Rajde, founder and chairman of Suvidhaa Infoserve.

At the back end of the system, Suvidhaa has created a credit profile based on transaction records. The technology platform keeps track of every transaction and remittance made, and then adds this to the profile of the consumer. The anticipative technology allows the lender to understand the profile of each customer. Armed with this knowledge, Suvidhaa can offer loans without hesitation to a class of migrant consumers who don't have the documents which a traditional banker would demand. As a result, consumers get overdraft facility at 15 per cent, a rate much lower than what a local money lender would charge.

Suvidhaa is enhancing the population of dependable borrowers. So far it has a database of 5,00,000 eligible borrowers and it hopes to scale it up to 3–4 million. Or to about 10 per cent of its 32 million unique customers.

This concept turns the financial inclusion approach on its head. Instead of looking for depositors, the system is creating borrowers. The real challenge here would be to scale up operations in a manner that benefits the entire system. In some ways, it complements the self-help groups and the joint liability group concept. It also takes it further by placing the onus of repayment on individuals without collective pressure, consequently creating millions of borrowers who understand the benefits of disciplined borrowing.

The numbers may look small but they indicate a huge potential for growth. This is reflected in the valuations of companies in the electronic payments business. Great Indian Retail Group was acquired by WireCard for $254 million while Billdesk is valued at $1 billion. These valuations reflect not just the importance of the electronic payments business, but its application in creating good borrowers.

If India can create higher numbers of good borrowers, it would ensure that every Indian would sooner or later be connected to the banking system and be part of the mainstream.

Financial transactions using online connections are routine. ATMs are ubiquitous, while credit cards that dominated retail sales may soon become redundant. Electronic wallets and digital money is rapidly replacing cash and credit card usage.

Effectively, financial technologies or fintech is changing all its various sub-sectors. These include banking, insurance, and stock markets. While existing consumers are moving to ever new ways of moving money, fintech is bringing millions – in money and in people – into the financial mainstream.

In its most fundamental impact, the use of cash is being reduced by newer methods. 'The transaction value for the Indian fintech sector is estimated to be approximately US $33 billion in 2016 and is forecast to reach US $73 billion in 2020, growing at a five-year CAGR of 22 per cent,' says a KPMG-Nasscom report on the future of fintech. The report says that seven key themes will lead the change. These are robo-advisory, P2P lending, bank in a box, security and biometrics, financial inclusion, next-generation payments, and blockchain.[2]

The government is encouraging the use of technology in the financial services and banking sector since it will bring more transparency in the system and undermine the parallel economy that runs mostly on illegal cash transactions.

Take a look at robo-advisors. These algorithm-based services replace age-old personal investment advice. Investors looking for suggestions on how to distribute their savings for maximum returns don't have to go to a financial advisor. They subscribe to a robo-advisory service and make their own portfolio. All that an investor has to do is to punch in the details of his earnings and his target earnings. The algorithm will throw up choices based on financial instruments available in the market. Companies offering such services are popular with the millennials. While they are becoming more popular in the US, several Indian companies are offering these services too. These companies include ScripBox, ArthaYantra, MyUniverse, and BigDecisions. These companies are not fringe players. They boast big partnerships, indicating the importance of the service. MyUniverse is owned by the Aditya Birla Group, while BigDecisions was bought by NewsCorp in 2014.

Advance payment systems technology is rapidly being deployed by smart start-ups. These include Simpel, FTCash, CitrusPay, and Kyash. Payments through mobiles and digital wallets are increasing rapidly and redefining banking. For millennials used to service at their fingertips, the banking system of even the late 1990s might seem an anachronism. For the adults of those years, however, it is the opposite. The last few years have seen technology change the face of banking to such an extent that it must seem alien to those who still prefer to transact over a counter at their neighbourhood branches.

And, technology is not being used just at the front end to bring consumers together. Banks in India are eagerly adopting automation, artificial intelligence, and machine learning to improve efficiency and increase quality of service to their consumers.

From the sixty-year-old State Bank of India to the few-months-old Bandhan Bank or the new-generation payment banks such as Airtel, Jio, and others, most progressive banks are adopting new technology solutions.

The largest private sector bank in India, ICICI Bank, has deployed software robotics in over 200 business processes of different functions at the bank. Software robotics refers to the combination of mechanical devices operated by closed software systems that perform a specific set of tasks. The bank claims that by using software robotics it has been able to reduce consumer response time by 60 per cent, achieving nearly 100 per cent accuracy. Over 10 lakh banking transactions are managed by the robotics every working day. 'The software robots at

ICICI Bank are configured to capture and interpret information from systems, recognize patterns, and run business processes across multiple applications to execute activities including data entry and validation, automated formatting, multi-format message creation, text mining, workflow acceleration, reconciliations, and currency exchange rate processing among others,' says the bank.[3]

Its MD and CEO, Chanda Kochhar, says the use of robots will rise rapidly within the bank. The business of the bank is growing at 25 per cent, and therefore such software will allow it to scale up rapidly without losing out on efficiency and quality of service.

DriveSmart by Bajaj Finserv

The insurance players in India are rapidly deploying technology for many operations. Of the fifty-three insurance companies in the country, twenty-four offer life, while twenty-nine are in non-life insurance, with General Insurance Corporation of India being the sole re-insurance company. Less than 2 per cent of healthcare expenses are covered by insurance, making this a highly untapped sector. Growth here is about 20 per cent per year. About 360 million life insurance policies are booked every year, with an annual growth of 15 per cent predicted for this segment in the next five years.

To manage this growth, companies in India have begun assessing the advantages of technologies like robotic process automation, machine learning, and blockchain, since most of the processes are highly repeatable. A KPMG report, Digital Disruption in the Insurance Industry, notes, 'The evolution and adoption of technology in the insurance sector has seen a tremendous growth. This has led to increase in penetration of the services to a larger audience leading towards holistic progression.' The report says that AI is changing the way customers interact with insurance businesses. Statistical and machine learning will form the processes in the future.[4]

The motor insurance space in India works on generic parameters even today, without any option for customer customization, thereby making it a 'one size fits all' concept. Its major emphasis is on price. At Bajaj Allianz General Insurance Company (BAGIC) there is constant effort taken to create holistic solutions that are dynamic to meet the changing requirements of the customer whilst also ensuring a seamless insurance transaction. Even though the size of the motor insurance portfolio for the company stands at ₹3,700 crore, it still uses generic parameters like vehicle make, model, and the location to decide the premium. These static variables in the proposal form do not provide a clear picture about the driving habits of the insured and do not factor in customer segmentation. Good drivers compensate for bad drivers and this has been the trend in a market which is highly price sensitive. For the customer, taking a motor insurance policy is still an obligation, on account of governing laws leaving little room for value addition.

To break this convention, BAGIC came out with DriveSmart, India's first telematics-based analytical service offering provided with a motor insurance policy. It is the first usage-based insurance policy in India enabled through big data analytics, monitoring, and giving real-time feedback on the customer's driving behaviour. The analysed data is used to price the insurance premium based on the driver and not entirely on the car or its location. The company has made a paradigm shift from vehicle-based pricing to customer-based pricing.

DriveSmart implements the latest digital and cloud-based technology. It has partnered with CarIQ, a Telematics solution provider, towards building systems to support the service. The company has invested ₹6 crore in this project. Its offering comes with a read-only hardware device that acts as a black box, which can be connected to the OBD-II port (standard port in all cars) of the car. The device collects the data from the port, which is then sent to the cloud. For this, the company has set up an IT infrastructure anchored in a public cloud. The channel for communication between the device and the cloud is encrypted, and all the advanced data analytics is carried out using the big data platform on cloud. The outcome of the analysed data is presented to customers in a user-friendly format, giving them information on their driving behaviour and patterns, and on the car's health. For this, the existing app of the company – Insurance Wallet – was integrated with the platform library. The app is also integrated to an on-premise data warehouse with Telematics platform so as to facilitate customer self-service capabilities like 24x7 roadside assistance, monitoring of battery and engine health, etc. The app empowers the customer and helps him/her to take precautionary measures, and also provides the customer with easy assistance in the event of an accident.

In a market where the average premium for private cars is anywhere between ₹7,000 and ₹8,000 a year, it is a challenge to provide a telematics-based offering at a competitive price. The

USP behind the telematics-based solution is to make DriveSmart an enabler towards inculcating better driving behaviour, thereby saving the customer fuel expenses, which is manifold in comparison with the discount on the insurance premium.

*

Internet-enabled Services

With the financial sector continuing to grow rapidly – thanks to innovative products and ambitious customers wanting to earn more than a safe interest on their deposits – the financial institutions got into a cycle of having to constantly upgrade their infrastructure to meet the demands. It did not help their bottom line that technology was evolving just as quickly, with high obsolescence (some of it perhaps deliberately built-in) and service and replacement costs.

The emergence of the Internet, and later the protocols that would ensure secure communications, made it easier to connect more branches, customers, and services to the daily operations. ATMs no longer needed to be physically close to a branch – all they needed was access to a telephone line.

This also created redundancies in the workforce at the branch levels. Why have many tellers when you can make do with just one or two, replacing the others with ATMs that cost less to the company compared to the lifetime cost of an employee? Why go through middlemen to post your trades when you could deal directly on the stock market? The resulting layoffs and voluntary retirement schemes created short-term pain for (at least the promise of) long-term savings.

Over the past few years, many financial institutions have looked to deal with their customers online rather than offline. Not only does this reduce the commitment of resources at physical touch-points (such as branches or outlets) but it also allows the company to address customer requirements faster, resulting in happier customers, using an optimal workforce. Portfolios have been dematerialized and can be managed online; bank accounts can be used just as easily as – in fact, even easier than – at the branch. In fact, some banks even mulled charging for in-branch transactions that could have been carried out through their websites.

Mobile Banking

In recent years, wireless data networks across the world have increased in quality to match those of wired services. At the same time, smartphones have become smarter and easier to use. Fingerprint-/face-scanners, found only on some of the most expensive business laptops five years ago, are now available on sub-₹13,000 smartphones. This affords smartphones a level of security hitherto unimagined; this also means they have enough safeguards in place to be trusted with a customer's bank details.

Every financial institution that has a mass-reach clientele is now working on improving the experience for its customers on the mobile phone. Their apps do everything, from pushing notifications about great deals – a key component of staying connected to the customer – to authenticating transactions through biometrics and/or PINs. It is now possible to enforce the same level of encryption (128 bit, which is the common standard, or even 256-bit, which is what the industry is moving towards) on a mobile device as on a dedicated terminal.

E-commerce and E-wallets

Considering the increase in access to the Internet seen in recent years, the growth in e-commerce is hardly surprising. In addition to the ease of buying things off an online catalogue (or booking services), the ability to pay online – and therefore avoid the hassle of being available in person at the time of delivery – has been a key reason for the sector's meteoric rise. This would not have happened if the banks had shied away from allowing online payments through merchants and third-party payment gateways.

But there is only so much an e-commerce solution can provide. In countries like India, where there is a definite sense of security in carrying hard currency, the recent demonetization move has come as a shot in the arm to start-ups like PayTM, Freecharge, and PhonePe. The technology now exists to quickly load up these electronic wallets with the amount needed, making settlements easier even when you don't have enough in your actual wallet. These e-wallets also offer a nice marketing channel for merchants to offer customized discounts to their customers. While these businesses still shy away from talking about sustainability and profitability in the long run, it is certain that, at least at the time of writing this book, they are looking to lodging themselves between the payee and payer.

Blockchain

The earliest electronic databases used were card- or file-based; this was superseded by relational databases where indexing was used to access data faster. However, the fundamental risk remained – these databases required robust and dynamic security measures to keep from being hacked, but also remained vulnerable to corruption among the gatekeepers. In other words, the keys to the data had to be entrusted to people who could, through an error or an act of deliberation, misuse the data itself.

Blockchain emerged as an alternative to these systems. First proposed by Satoshi Nakamoto in 2010, the idea was soon implemented as a core component on the bitcoin system. A blockchain, as the name suggests, is a chain of blocks containing data. These blocks are replicated over a peer-to-peer network, thus 'democratizing' access while preventing modification of existing data by constantly comparing it with other blocks containing the original information. There is no one with the power to alter the data after a transaction has been recorded; there is no need to seek permission from anyone to use a blockchain database because its very nature prevents the core data from being corrupted.

In other words, it is a distributed database that always has multiple images of itself located in different nodes – in the sending bank, the receiving bank, the client's cloud, etc. Each image is used as a reference point to check an illegal entry.

ICICI Bank has become the first bank in India to use blockchain technology. The bank proudly announced it had completed an export-related transaction in minutes instead of days using blockchain. In October 2016, ICICI Bank worked with Emirates NBD to begin using this technology. It transferred trade documents and money, and conducted transactions using blockchain. These transfers related to purchase order, shipping, insurance, invoice, etc., which are regular documents in any international trade deal. While traditionally it can take days for these documents to be sent, verified, and registered with related parties, with blockchain the process took minutes, says the bank. In a world of fluctuating foreign exchange rates, speed of transaction assures certainty for both buyer and seller. Large banks such as ICICI will be increasingly relying on blockchain to ensure speed and security of transactions.

In the past few months, the interest in blockchain technology has risen exponentially. In fact, in many conferences it is now the buzzword, and is seen as the next big development in fintech. The WannaCry ransomware attack, in which the hackers are reported to have asked for bitcoins in order to return control of the compromised terminals, put the spotlight on blockchain, the technology that is used by many crypto-currencies even in the civilian space that's normally uninterested in such technical matters. With more and more countries coming to accept crypto-currencies as legal tender (Japan in February 2017, Australia in July 2017), banks are already commissioning development of in-house systems based on this technology.

Peer-to-Peer (P2P) Lending

Modelled on the P2P model of file-sharing, P2P lending matches lenders and borrowers who meet each other's requirements. While this is more of an innovation on the service side of things – the financial institution finding a way to service a customer it does not want to lose, even if it may not want to back that customer itself – the application of the technology has finally added layers of security to a practice that dates back to the time when electricity wasn't even dreamt of. The mediating institution collects a commission, the lender does not have to do the due diligence which is the institution's responsibility, and the borrower can raise funds without going to the grey market.

*

Monexo: P2P Lending on Cloud

P2P lending is not new since people have been lending and borrowing from each other for centuries. The structure around the formal P2P model allows strangers to connect with each other for borrowing and lending, with both benefiting in some way. Monexo Innovations is among the companies that have begun P2P lending in India.

Monexo has created a technology platform that matches borrowers with lenders. Let's say a young professional has about ₹10 lakh to invest. He or she can invest in traditional instruments like fixed deposits, equity, or mutual funds. After that the professional has about ₹2,00,000 left over.

The professional will register with Monexo and offer details about the money available to lend. The money is then deposited with partner bank IDBI. Monexo's system will run a match for him and suggest borrowers.

Now comes the interesting part. Getting lenders is easy but finding good borrowers is not. This is where the technology platform plays a role. When one looks at the brick-and-mortar process, the customer has to go to the branch and apply for the loan. Someone in the bank then checks his application form and other relevant documents. After that the bank officials take a decision on whether to sanction the loan.

At Monexo, the decision is made by the system based on data. As soon as the borrower applies for a loan, all the relevant data about him is uploaded. This also includes his personal profile from social media like Facebook. The software checks the borrower's PAN income tax card, Aadhaar card, and connects with his salary account. Monexo will seek the account details from the borrower's bank with permission. The borrower will have to upload the account statement. Once this is done, the Monexo system will automatically check the borrower's earning and spending details.

Monexo would have read the electronic bank statement and seen whether in the last ninety days the borrower got the same salary from the same company. It will check the borrower's expense pattern and assess whether he or she is living within his or her means.

It tracks the borrower's credit card payments and sees the past record of repayment of the borrower. Most importantly, the software checks the borrower's willingness to repay. Often, borrowers have the capability but not the willingness to repay loans. Monexo trawls through social media to assess the borrower's personality profile. Its system then makes an assessment based on the personality that emerges.

Once the system is satisfied, the loan is approved and the borrower is matched with a lender. Most importantly, the interest rate is flexible and is based on the risk profile of the borrower. The more information available to the system and the better the track record, the lower the interest rate.

'All this happens on a real-time basis,' says Mukesh Bubna, founder of Monexo. 'We want to serve a different segment of the market, which is underserved, and where we can add value and bring down its price for them. Because our efficiency of process, the benefits will get passed on to borrowers, and the lenders will be happy with the personalized customer care.'

Fintech has created the biggest kranti in India. It has disrupted the banking and telecom sectors. In many ways, the walls between financial services and telecom services companies have been brought down. Mobile payment firm PayTM began as a technology company, converted into a mobile wallet, and is now a bank. The next growth will be in the insurance sector. But the services of banking and insurance will be so tech-led that it will make older banks like HDFC Bank and ICICI Bank appear outdated.

The government's efforts to create a digital payment ecosystem is likely to ensure that financial services in India could soon create history. More than 24 million unbanked people have opened bank accounts in the last two years. And the figure is rising. No other country would have brought so many people into the financial mainstream using technology in such a short time.

9

AGRICULTURE AND FOOD

Cargill Harvests Mobile Trading

Enter Pritech Business Park in Bengaluru, and it looks like any other cluster of glass and steel buildings that house hundreds of offices and companies, global and local. In one of the buildings is the offices of Cargill Business Services (CBS), the lesser known unit of the $107 billion global giant, Cargill Inc. The US-based company provides agriculture, food, and related services to markets worldwide. In Bengaluru, it set up its India office in 2015.

While CBS runs several units, in one corner of one of the offices sits a compact team that worries about how to make the entire process smoother, faster, and tech-enabled – from procurement to pricing to storage to delivery and finally, consumption. The team is constantly working on ways to use new technology in a sector that has been woefully devoid of it. The CBS team has been working on solutions that involve drones, automated contracts, and mobile-based solutions that are reducing the time from harvest to consumption for many categories of grains and seeds. From traders to consumers, each link of the agricultural chain is being infused with technology-led processes.

Says Siraj Chaudhry, CEO of Cargill in India: 'Introduction of technology has enabled improved decision making, reduced hunch or previous experience-based decision making. It has brought in more accountability into the system. People cannot hide behind excuses. There is better objective decision making and greater control across the system. Once you have these systems in place, it is very easy for people to identify where the decision-making sits.'

Great products are often the result of great work by multiple teams on multiple levels. That was the case with Cargill's Agriculture Supply Chain (CASC) India team, who recently developed and deployed an innovative new mobile app designed to automate highly manual and time-consuming tasks.

Identifying a problem can create a significant opportunity to improve the status quo. In this case, the team knew it was wasting too much time on inefficient processes and redundant tasks (such as manual interventions or reconciliations) that were costing the business both time and money. In addition to their inefficiency, the supporting processes lacked clarity regarding the status of new deal origination and trade terms. The team knew there had to be a better way, so they set out to find one, partnering with CBS Bangalore to streamline their commodity-origination process. The result was a new innovative mobile app, mProcure.

Most commodity negotiations in India happen in the fields. Due to absence of connectivity in remote areas, a user is not able to conduct his/her business using an application that would require network connectivity. CASC India decided a mobile app would be the most feasible solution. The advantage of this mobile application is that it can be used in areas where there is no network connectivity at all; the users can carry on their business and enter the transactions into the app, which would then sync with the server when the user returns to an area where network is available.

In August 2014, the business partnered with the global IT mobility team at CBS Bangalore to develop the mProcure mobile app. The project represented two materially different ways of working. It was the first project to use the API gateway for security authentication and the first application to be developed from scratch by the mobility team in CBS Bangalore. The app is also unique because it has both a web version for traders and an app version for originators.

The mobile app makes it possible for merchants in the field to enter procurement details in real-time on a tablet that integrates into their legacy commodity trading system. With mProcure, merchants no longer needed desktops, laptops or networks to enter procurement details into the Cargill system. The app also eliminated the need to prepare daily procurement reports – it enabled seamless flow of information and timely calculation of mark-to-market and daily income statements between other systems.

For a long time, agriculture across the world was marked by intensive physical labour as input. The advent of powerful machines, especially after the Second World War, saw the

Western countries, which had access to these technologies without price barriers, embrace them gladly. The spirit of enterprise that they were able to afford resulted in machine-driven, large-scale farming that was capital-driven but more productive than in other parts of the world. Governments also started to promote modern techniques such as crop rotation, soil replenishment, etc.

Conversely, in India, land reforms meant that holdings were carved up into smaller units that made economies of scale difficult. With agriculture not being one of the 'preferred' professions, education was seen as something that entitled you to a 'better' profession such as engineering or medicine. The consequence, of course, was that one of the most critical industries that drives any nation suffered due to ignorance and lack of awareness about modern tools and techniques. Farmers were not trained in ways that could maximize their fields' productivity.

It was not just ignorance that held the industry back, however. In rural areas, in the absence of minimum-wage guarantees, the low cost of labour made manpower a more attractive proposition than the costlier investments in equipment. However, with recent trends in migration of this labour force from rural to urban areas, this scenario is likely to change. This is a long-term evolution, though, while the need of the hour is a faster solution to address the widening gap between demand and supply of healthy, properly-grown food.

The Indian farmer's dependence on the monsoons is also well known across the world. Irrigation remains a perennial problem, although the situation has eased up – with the exception of droughts – in the past decade and a half.

With the focus back on safety and health, thanks to increased awareness on the part of the consumers, organic farming solutions have become increasingly popular. However, this is yet to reach industry-scale – perhaps it might never get there – but farmers, especially urban farmers who can afford the larger investment that organic farming needs, are adopting 'greener' ways of growing their produce, eschewing pesticides, genetically-modified seeds, and other chemicals that might prove harmful to the environment.

Satellite-enabled support for everything, from agricultural inputs (best time to plant, what crops to use, variants, weather forecasts, etc.) to damage assessment (pest, wildlife, natural calamities, drought, etc.) to topography mapping (to regularize land holdings) is also helping those who can afford these solutions to plan their planting schedules better. Efforts are on to increase functional literacy so that farmers will be able to use computers/mobile devices and access information themselves.

The travesty of the Indian economy is that the biggest sector in the country is most deprived of technology. The sector supports almost 50 per cent of the population and accounts for 17 per cent of gross value added in the economy.

Despite being second only to China in terms of investment in agricultural R&D, there have not been any commensurate improvements in the field in India. Underutilization of funds, combined with the persistence of outdated techniques (either out of stubbornness or ignorance or a combination of both) means that the Indian farmer is still dependent on a lot of factors beyond his control when it comes to his crops.

Much of the infusion of technology has been on seeds and new varieties. Issues regarding genetically modified seeds are still to be resolved. Mechanization has picked up, but inadequate financial models and fragmented holdings still create complexities.

In India, large companies in the agricultural sector have begun to use technology across different parts of the value chain. At the same time, scores of young start-ups are exploring innovative new solutions. While the large companies tend to focus on their own business, they have scale. The young ones may not have scale but are not bound by any business interests. They are keen to attack any problem that they find exciting enough.

Ajay Vir Jakhar, chairman of farmer body Bharat Krishak Samaj, has many suggestions as to where technology can play a role in agriculture:

- The government is creating a 'nationally consistent database' to be made available at a nominal cost to all stakeholders.
- Prioritization of preventive measures, as is being delivered by NDDB and AMUL rather than targeting disease cure. Animal health is a major driver of disease in humans.
- Individual household bio-gas units.
- Incentivization of farm machinery leasing services so farmers get to use good farm machinery without having to own machinery. This will increase productivity by up to 20 per cent while minimizing use of inputs.
- Improvement of Indian Metrological Department's medium-term (specifically) weather forecasts for agriculture.

These are priorities that the private sector is also excited about. So much so that Cargill built its mProcure system banking on the fact that curing these inefficiencies could, by itself, be a route to profitability. Launched in October 2015, mProcure is now live in India across six states and for four commodities.

Let's see how mProcure works. Traders start using the app by creating a buying plan that includes quantities, amounts, and locations of the commodities to be procured. They then assign these commodities to originators or field reps, who negotiate and finalize deals with suppliers or farmers.

After back-and-forth negotiations, traders approve the deals and originators complete the trade information forms with such details as cost of freight, shipping, taxes, packaging, suppliers, brokers, and more. Once approved, the final purchase contracts are sent to the traders and originators, completing the origination processes for procurement.

The app features trader and position reports to better understand the current and future cash position, which enables improved advance procurement planning. The app's contract-amendment feature automatically regenerates the contract and allows easy editing of contract parameters. According to Cargill, the app has achieved a nearly 100 per cent adoption rate among users, with over 2,600 purchase contracts generated from the mobile app at the time of my conversation with them.

When the originator was travelling, the purchase contract generation would take two to three days, depending on when the originator returned to the back office. Now the purchase contract can be generated in a few hours, including the time taken for negotiations.

mProcure was designed to be operable even by a non-technical person such as a trader, originator or accountant. It automates previously manual tasks, works in both online and offline modes, and provides traders, originators and accountants the opportunity to focus on more value-added tasks.

For someone not used to the process, this might seem an obvious, almost routine process. It becomes significant only when you consider how these deals were executed until now.

In the past, origination (or procurement) was done manually. Traders sitting in a distant office would take positions on a day-to-day basis while assessing reports and data from trading news and platforms. They would communicate with originators (or agents) in the field over the telephone. They would jot down points in their notebooks or diaries. Now these originators would work with merchants in the field and have a negotiations-type of procurement. That information would them be sent back to the head office for the people on the trading platform, who would then enter this data manually on the platform. Documents would be generated for the origination or procurement of the grain.

The whole process took about a week because of the back-and-forth that happened, the double checking of figures, confirming of figures, etc. This was a pain point because it took a lot of time and also led to errors. There were tricky situations where people would challenge figures that had been poorly communicated. Now mProcure has done away with all these issues. The application has two components – a web component and a tablet component. Through the web component, the traders in the head office can determine at what price a particular commodity has to be purchased, and they can send that information to the originators in the field, who receive it in real-time on their tablets.

From one week to generate a contract, mProcure has brought the time to completion down to a few hours. The moment the negotiations are done the contract is generated and sent as a PDF file to all the stakeholders. Cargill says the utilization of this digital system means 75 per cent of the work is done. While this technology is applied in Maharashtra, Uttar Pradesh, Haryana, and Rajasthan, other states will benefit too. Agri-products like soya, oil seeds, wheat, and other grain are being procured using mProcure.

Cargill is also using such technology on the sales end to track consumer purchase behaviour for its different products.

*

A critical stage for the agricultural process is the commodity market. We are witnessing transformational change with the onset of digital technology, and agriculture is no exception. India accounts for 7.68 per cent of the total global agricultural output. The contribution of agriculture to the Indian economy is much higher than world average. After the milestone green and white revolutions, the most recent revolution in the country is in information and communication technology (ICT).

ICT has had an impact on every aspect of business across all industries, including farming. It has made significant inroads in a traditional agrarian economy like India. The Indian agro-sector has been exploiting the benefits of ICT. Innovative ICT application platforms are being created by private sector players in conjunction with local farmers, who are embracing technology and digital communications to not only manage farm operations but to also change the way they manage crops and livestock. The phenomenon of e-agriculture is a new one – one that is having a rapid and dramatic impact on food production and farming.

The traditional focus on improving productivity has meant that technology has been used in precision agriculture, inputs, machinery, and more. Farm animals are being fed and monitored using electronic sensors and identification systems. In the past few years, there has been increasing use of technology in post-harvest management and in the marketing of agri-produce too.

NCDEX's Electronic Exchange

The National Commodity Exchange (NCDEX) is increasingly using technology to leapfrog into the future since the agriculture sector has not utilized technology to its full potential. Being at the centre of this development, NCDEX has played an important role in catalysing this change. It has married technology with financial market infrastructure and the value chain ecosystem to create and enhance agri-commodity networks and platforms for bringing customers the benefit of scale, transparency, and ease of doing business. Technology has been used to create large platforms for spot trading, auctions, derivatives trading, dematting commodities, for creating e-pledges, e-warehouse receipts, building social communities, offering services such as 'book my warehouse', online repository services, creating a data hub for agri-businesses, and the like.

Dematting Commodities, Electronic Accounting

NCDEX pioneered electronic accounting of commodities in the country, dematting commodities through the creation of COMTRACK, an electronic web-based system which facilitates electronic accounting of commodities deposited in the warehouses approved by the Exchange. It connects the Exchange, warehouses, assayers, members, investors, and clients.

Taking cues from the success of this project, Warehousing Development and Regulatory Authority (WDRA) has issued licences to set up a new repository of all warehouses. NCDEX group company, NCDEX e-Repository Limited (NERL), is one of the two organizations which has been selected for the same. It started operations in 2017.

The benefits of switching to electronic accounting are almost immediate and lie in speed, ease of use, accuracy, and cost. Automation reduces overheads and man-hours, with document transmission constrained only by the speed of the Internet. The commodity repository will provide the legal and regulatory environment for inventory financing and warehouse receipt lending to encourage the use of these financing mechanisms.

Warehouse financing is a crucial enabler in the holistic development of agricultural markets, and an electronic registry – which provides for transparency and tracking of commodities in every single warehouse – will go a long way in giving comfort to banks. This can be the single biggest game changer for the industry.

Unified Market Platform (UMP) – Creation of a Modern Mandi *Platform*

Traditionally, middlemen have always been the bane of farmers. The farmer has never been able to see improved outcomes on account of his dependency on the middleman to sell his produce. Agriculture Produce Market Committee (APMC) markets or registered mandis suffer from fragmentation and lack of price transparency.

NCDEX, through its group company NCDEX eMarkets Limited (NeML), has spearheaded the modernization and digitalization of regulated primary agricultural markets, commonly known as APMC/Mandi. Using the 'one state one market' building block, it has helped transform the regulated, fragmented APMC markets in Karnataka into a single state agricultural market (SAM) using its Unified Market Platform (UMP®). Created in partnership with the Government of Karnataka, which has set up Rashtriya eMarket Services (ReMS), currently 157 mandis in Karnataka use e-trading, e-permits, e-payments, and scientific grading and assaying services. In Andhra Pradesh, the company, in association with the state government and ReMS has brought the ten largest APMC markets in the state, including Guntur, to online trading. The plan is for the system to be handed over to the state government after it has stabilized.

This initiative has helped bring transparency in price discovery, efficiency in operations, cost savings, and increase in realizations for its users, who range from farmers and traders to mandis and government agencies. It has positively impacted the lives of more than 15 million farmers in the three states under UMP.

e-Auction Platform

Technology is also being increasingly used to bring transparency, efficiency, and national reach to producers. The trading platforms combine technological efficiency and market-friendly trading features in a transparent atmosphere to make trading a rich and rewarding experience for the stakeholders.

NeML helps state governments and government agencies with a credible and full-service platform to procure from producers across the country, resulting in savings in both time and money. A complete solution is provided, including trade-facilitation, collateral management, logistics, supply chain management, and clearing and settlement. NeML positively impacted more than 35 million consumers in various states under food security programmes. It remains committed to leveraging e-markets for farmers and below-poverty-line (BPL) consumers.

It has used technology to build market access for producers of fruits and vegetables. NeML has created market linkages for apple, strawberry, kinnow, and litchi farmers from Maharashtra, Himachal Pradesh, Bihar, Rajasthan and Punjab, and connected them with national buyers. NeML has also established a national dairy e-market for National Cooperative Dairy Federation of India by efficiently leveraging technology.

Book My Warehouse App

The Exchange offers an online automated system of warehouse booking – 'Book-My-Warehouse' – available on the NCDEX app as well, making it more convenient for market participants. This online Warehouse Space Reservation (WSR) system allows registered customers of the Exchange to view and book warehouse space online. Depositors can check availability and book space in their warehouse of choice with a click from the convenience of their home, office or even right from the field through smartphones.

A first-of-its-kind initiative in the country, this real-time service has enhanced ease of doing business. There are over one million tonnes of commodities that are annually deposited on the exchange platform, and the Exchange has a network of over 400 approved warehouses. This system has brought greater transparency and efficiency to the warehousing system, helping warehouse service providers to better utilize warehouse capacity, and helping customers to accrue savings in time and money.

At the back-end of this functionality is integration with COMTRACK, the Exchange's proprietary electronic commodity accounting system. The facility is also available on the 'NCDEX-Markets' mobile app through the 'Book-My-Warehouse' tab. NCDEX-Markets app is available on Apple Store, Google Playstore, and Windows Store.

The WSR system will aid in changing old practices of crop storage and help to raise farmer incomes, thereby bringing both macro and micro economic benefits. The system brings relief to depositors who experience long waiting periods outside warehouses during peak harvest season and find it difficult to locate empty warehouses.

Using WSR, farmers can locate and book an appropriate warehouse well in time to adequately store their agricultural produce and thus seek a better price for their produce. The facility also allows warehouse service providers to better utilize their capacity.

With a booking window open from 10 a.m. to 12.30 p.m., the WSR system permits reservation of space for up to 500 metric tonnes per warehouse per day, giving an equal opportunity to every depositor. Clients are allowed to initiate a 'wait list' request in case of non-availability of space in their selected warehouse.

Furthermore, embedded email alerts help clients keep track of their booking status.

Tracking of Goods and Enhanced Security through RFID

Radio Frequency Identification (RFID) and similar wireless technologies are increasingly finding use in tracking and security of agricultural produce.

RFID ensures that the commodities stored in the warehouses are tracked through radio frequency signals and this real-time information helps improve the efficiency and reliability of the storage and delivery operations at the warehouses.

NCDEX is the first commodity exchange in the world to use this technology for the goods stored in its approved warehouses. With a pilot done for storing guar gum in Bikaner, the exchange plans to introduce it in a phase-wise manner across all delivery centres.

Next-Generation Trading and Surveillance

NCDEX has constantly striven to increase market efficiency and transparency through technology that elevates performance. This technology is also easy to use. The Exchange has recently revamped its trading and surveillance system, bringing greater convenience, speed, safety, and transparency to the market.

Among the country's fastest trading systems, it brings a more dynamic experience to users, with features such as tick-by-tick broadcast and ease of executing complex trading strategies. With order execution enhanced by five times, it is also better suited to offer products such as options and indices, besides handling high frequency/algorithm trading. Fortified with a large processing capacity of 1,000 orders per second (which can go up to 3,000 orders per second), the NextGen system supports the Financial Information Exchange (FIX) protocol, which is the industry norm. Built on highly specialized fault-tolerant technology, its replica processes ensure uninterrupted trading even in the face of software or hardware outages. It has been developed by MillenniumIT, the leading ultralow-latency technology provider and part of the London Stock Exchange Group.

Informed Decision-making

Digital devices are increasingly being used by farmers in agricultural marketing for making use of informed decisions. The market price information widely disseminated through various digital platforms including ticker boards, websites, TV channels and, more recently, mobile apps, helps value chain participants make informed decisions that promote efficient production and trade. It is especially valuable for the farmers who sell their produce in local and regional markets. Such crucial information helps them negotiate better with traders, determine what markets to sell to, store their crops until price increase, or even plan for future crops. This system also facilitates spatial distribution of products, from rural areas to towns and even between markets.

Though Internet penetration in rural India is less than 20 per cent, the next wave of growth is expected to come from there due to growth in cheaper smartphone handsets, spread of wireless networks, and evolving consumer behaviour. There are several mobile apps, developed by both the public and private sector, available for the farmer, helping him with information and advice about his produce.

The government of India now operates two mobile applications 'AgriMarket' and 'Crop Insurance' that enable farmers to get information related to crop insurance and prices of agri-commodities in different mandis across the country. NCDEX offers two apps – 'NCDEX markets' and 'NCDEX official' app – with over 16,000 users. Futures and spot market prices are extensively disseminated through these apps as well as through WhatsApp and SMS.

Data Tools for Financial Players

The commodity trading sector has witnessed significant changes over the past few years. Faced with tighter trading margins, lower volatility across most commodities, enhanced regulatory pressure, and a more complex trading environment, traders and financial institutions are required to alter their trading strategies dynamically. This is where data tools come in handy.

The rise of real-time, high-frequency trading has regulatory compliance teams working hard to keep pace with the industry's widening pools of structured and unstructured data. By employing emerging tools and techniques, and capital/commodity, markets firms can improve trade surveillance and spot abuse and irregularities before they can do harm.

Charting and Analysis Tools

NCharts brings together real-time market data, charting, and analytics to help one better manage price and trade risk. It includes coverage of the futures, spot, and spread charts.

Pre-trade analysis can be done on NCharts using charts and various reports. The NCharts pre-trade information tool enables traders/research analysts to search for the commodities they wish to trade in and identify an appropriate time and price in an efficient and effective manner. The pre-trade information tool significantly increases the probability of a successful trade and improves the efficiency of the execution workflow process.

Historical Back-testing and Stimulation of Trading Strategies

With the availability of tick-by-tick trading and historical data, NCharts can back-test trading strategies, which helps in building future strategies and maximizing profits.

Trade Analysis Using Liquidity Scheduler

The liquidity discovery tool enables dealers to market inventory and helps a trader to take positions by providing him concise liquidity/depth details of the commodity being traded.

IT Approach – Fertile Ground for RMAD

The NCDEX IT team took up the challenge to design a platform that would make it possible for all stakeholders in the physical commodity markets to conveniently book space in modern, safe, and regulated godowns run by some of the biggest warehouse operators in the country.

A solution called Rapid Mobile Application Development (RMAD), created by US-based service provider Apps Freedom, was used. This tool allows the development of a single unified app that can be downloaded from Apple Store, Google Playstore, and Windows Store.

Use of the RMAD tool not only brought down the developmental cost by three times but also simplified the system greatly. The WSR app was developed and implemented at great speed, and was rolled out in six weeks across three platforms with a team of only three developers. The app development work commenced in September 2015 and the pilot was successfully carried out in November 2015.

NextGen Trading System

NCDEX was promoted by NSE and ICICI Bank in 2003. Most of its systems, including the trading and surveillance system, were inherited from NSE. At that time, NSE systems were already thirteen years old. By the time NCDEX finished ten years, it was running a twenty-three-year-old system.

In 2014, the Exchange decided to revamp its trading infrastructure with state-of-the-art world-class architecture, in keeping with its vision and growth plans. SEBI taking charge of the commodity markets also meant stronger regulation aligned with the financial markets in the country. With new products like options and indices on the cards, the Exchange decide to upgrade its core infrastructure to cater to the growing market demand.

It was the biggest IT project that the Exchange had embarked on, with two core systems migrating to a completely new product and corresponding changes to eighteen downstream systems.

In 2015, NCDEX signed up with the London Stock Exchange-owned, Colombo-based, Millennium Technologies Software for this project.

Challenges

The road to implementation was very tough, keeping in mind that the Exchange not only had to change its core systems, but also had to change the eighteen downstream systems that derived their data from the main trading engine. Moreover, NCDEX decided to upgrade the market infrastructure by mandating the internationally-benchmarked FIX protocol as the only messaging standard to communicate with the market. This meant that along with the Exchange, all its brokers too had to upgrade their trading software to interface with NCDEX over the FIX Messaging standard. The entire project now assumed gigantic proportions.

Upgrading NCDEX to a FIX infrastructure meant that brokers could now employ international front-end systems, as that software was already FIX-compliant. Moreover, the FIX messaging standards gave better flexibility and security to transactions that were conducted on a daily basis.

The project involved a technical migration to a new trading and surveillance platform provided by Millennium Technologies.

It required a functional migration, involving introduction of a new Simplified Spreads contract with different business rules that was made available only in the new engine.

The project also entailed a market migration. The new trading engine was made available in FIX protocol only, forcing the market participants to migrate their front-office systems to a more modern FIX protocol.

And most importantly, all three migrations had to be done simultaneously.

Other exchanges had made the new trading engine available on both the old and the new protocols in order to avoid the complications of a simultaneous market migration.

The Exchange employed the 'risk upfront' philosophy, where instead of waiting for an event to happen and its corresponding risk to play out, it forced the event to mitigate the risks upfront. This would mean that any factor due to which something could go wrong was made live before the new trading engine went live.

The main mantra for the IT team to achieve this feat was 'extreme collaboration'. The IT team at NCDEX was working with MIT, a new partner. It was important to establish trust between the teams, considering the nature and gestation period of the project.

The 'risk upfront' philosophy made the exchange collaborate early with third-party software vendors as well as with data-feed providers like Reuters and Bloomberg. All partners appreciated the hand-holding provided by the NCDEX IT team in order to help them successfully connect to the new trading engine.

The NextGen system is among the country's fastest trading systems. It brings a more dynamic experience to users, with features such as tick-by-tick broadcast and ease of executing complex trading strategies. It speeds up by five times to order execution, bringing greater convenience, speed, safety, and transparency to the market.

Fortified with a large processing capacity of 1,000 orders per second, and built on highly specialized fault-tolerant technology, its replica processes ensure uninterrupted trading even in the face of software or hardware outages.

The NextGen trading platform is also better suited to offer products such as options and indices, besides having enough capacity to handle algorithmic trading (high-frequency trading). Additionally, it will be able to execute regulatory changes more quickly and cost-effectively, which will assist in efficient intra-day closure, pre-order checks, and order-flow monitoring.

The new surveillance system gives ample flexibility for NCDEX to monitor markets real-time, detect trading patterns, and address anomalies instantly.

Costs have also gone down, with the new systems having an open architecture, leading to reduction in operational expenses. The earlier system was a mainframe-equivalent system that had high maintenance costs.

The market realized the benefits of the system, and this helped tremendously. A total of twelve mock sessions were conducted, in which all brokers participated. There were monthly meetings with the software vendors who were coached to adjust with the new FIX format. As a result, the go-live was a non-event, and till date no production issue or downtime has happened on the trading or surveillance systems.

The use of genetically-modified crops/seeds has always been a contentious issue, and perhaps nowhere more so than in an economy like India's that is so heavily dependent on agriculture. Proponents point towards the benefits, and the critics, naturally, point to the unintended consequences that are sometimes worse than before man tampered with nature's gene codes. A case in point was the whitefly infestation that destroyed hectares and hectares of genetically-modified Bt cotton crops in north India in 2015.

However, given that the field is relatively new, few governments – including the Indian central government – are willing to take a leap of faith on genetically modified (GM) crops without due diligence, even in the face of overwhelming pressure from the international community and, particularly, the strong lobbying efforts of Monsanto, the American agricultural company specializing in GM seeds. Much of the public's distrust of GM crops stems from the fact that there is no guarantee that the long-term effects of consuming such foods will not be harmful.

Thankfully, the use of equipment is an entirely different – and much more straightforward – matter. With sanctions easing up and import laws in this sector too being eased up, farmers are getting access to modern equipment that has made farming easier and more productive in the West. Indian manufacturers no longer enjoy a monopoly and are, therefore, being pushed towards being more competitive both in terms of quality and pricing.

It isn't just heavy equipment that's changing the scene in India. Drones are now being pressed into service for capturing topographic data, crop detailing, etc. With more and more start-ups entering this field and offering specialized technical expertise – such as water quality control, air-dispersal of nutrients, automatic/sensor-controlled motors, etc. – the Indian farmer is in for exciting times ahead.

*

The Indian agricultural industry is in turmoil today. The farming community is grappling with challenges such as low productivity and slim profit margins. This sector, which meets the food and nutritional requirements of 1.3 billion Indians and employs 200 million, is in the doldrums.

Consider these figures: though India ranks third in production of rice, its yield is lower than Brazil's, China's, and the United States'. It is the same situation with pulses, where India is the second highest producer. India's rice yield is 2.4 tonnes per hectare, placing it 27th among forty-seven countries.[1]

A major obstacle that the Indian agriculture industry faces, besides erratic rains, is the size of its farm holdings. Over 67 per cent of the farms are holdings of less than one hectare. The farms of over 10 hectares make for only 1 per cent of the farms in India.[2]

In the US, it is the other extreme, the average farm being of 442 hectares. Over the years the number of farms there has reduced while average acreage has risen.[3]

In India, agricultural land holdings continue to shrink and this is a cause for concern. The total number of operational holdings in India stands at 138.35 million; out of them, 85 per cent are marginal and small farms. The average Indian farm is likely to shrink further between 2010 and 2021, says a government of India report titled, 'State of Indian Agriculture, 2015-16'.[4]

The Big Problem with Being a Small Farmer

Firstly, economies of scale are not achievable with small land holdings. The small farmer just cannot buy tractors or dispensers, let alone hi-tech machines, or hire an international agronomist. The two-acre Indian farms are simply technologically deprived. With zero science, the farmer operates his farm at a low efficiency. For example, in India, a hectare of land yields 16.4 metric tonnes of potato, while in the UK one hectare generates 44.7 tonnes of potato. The same land area will produce three times more in New Zealand.

Unlike the Western farmer with mega farms of hundreds of hectares manned by a slew of university graduates and artificial intelligence-powered robots like the Blue River ones smartly zipping around the fields, most Indian farmers are still in the stone age.

*

Internet Farms by Aibono

Vivek Rajkumar, a young millennial and grandson of a thriving farmer in southern Kerala, decided to reshape the destiny of the Indian farmer. An engineering design graduate from IIT, this entrepreneur audaciously set out to understand why the Indian farmer was stuck in a rut and could not revive his ancestral legacy. The farming industry, a crucial part of the Indian economy, was 'broken', and the tech-driven Rajkumar wanted to fix it.

As he spent time in the fields, Rajkumar found that some farmers were relying on a local expert who was dishing out a standard 'recipe' to grow crops and vegetables. Rajkumar decided to introduce new practices using technology, affordable Internet, and smartphones for affordable support. He also tapped into a pool of young, technologically savvy people adept in cloud computing.

Rajkumar started his company, Aibono, using capital he received from seed funders. 'Ai' signifies artificial intelligence and 'bono', in Latin, means 'good' implying the use of technology for the greater good.

Aibono virtually aggregates a number of farms on a cloud platform and provides them with a host of Internet services. The company is introducing IoT in small farms. This allows measurement application methods such as precision agriculture to use precise amounts of inputs for a crop, and Cyber Physical Share, made popular by sharing services such as Uber and food-ordering apps in the country. The advanced technological inputs provided by Aibono empowers the farmer by giving him control over external variables like weather, water, and soil inputs. From testing soil to informing the farmer about the time intervals at which they had to switch on their water sprinklers, Aibono is their friendly neighbourhood virtual associate, giving them daily inputs on what is to be done in their farm.

The backdrop of Aibono is a virtual copy of the physical farm on the common cloud platform. The data from the farm, transmitted through sensors and images, is analysed, and the inputs required are gauged. For instance, Aibono helps the farmer decide how much nitrogen will be required per day for his crop.

Inputs like fertilizers or water are measured and fed, and the response is also studied to assess a field's productivity. Drones are also deployed to check for crop diseases and the weather closely monitored.

When a farmer logs in, Aibono, whose mascot is a smiling seed, hand-holds him on his crop decisions, helps him with information on agricultural inputs, data science, on-ground tech support, and much more. And, in the process, it helps the farmers multiply their yields many times over. Aibono doesn't charge a fee but asks the farmers to share a small percentage of their harvest.

More than 200 small farmers in six villages in the hilly Western Ghats area have signed up on Aibono's software platform. Effectively, this helps them overcome the limitations of farm size. The 200 small farms together become one big smart farm where services are common and therefore affordable.

These farmers, who now belong to one community, can now share anything from a tractor to information on effective fertilizers in the market. Under Aibono's Smart Platform, a small farmer is able to afford a hi-tech machine and expert advice on modern methods of farming.

Once a farmer signs up, a Cyber Physical Liaison is assigned to him to assist him on the ground for ninety days. One hundred farmers share a bunch of managers/agents and resources such as farm measurements and soil-testing devices.

The first step involves the agent suggesting the best crop to be planted based on weather, soil, and market forecast. A ninety-day schedule is drawn up with task dashboards, and the farm's data is loaded on to the platform. As the days unfold, agents visit the farm regularly, click pictures, and feed information onto the platform. They connect to crop doctors and AI engines to figure out what is best for the crop on a regular basis. Armed with this information, the agents advise the farmers on the 'precise' amount of nutrients or water they need to apply to their crop. A drone is sometimes dispatched to check for crop diseases.

Let's take a farmer who is generating one tonne of lettuce during a single sixty-day harvest from his quarter acre of land. His cost of production is ₹12,000–₹15,000 and his revenue ₹25,000. After the farmer is convinced to join Aibono's platform, he gets the benefits of being on a cloud platform with precision agriculture, AI, and data analytics thrown in. At the end of the cycle, his small farm yields 3 tonnes of lettuce and he earns ₹65,000. Delighted with his new income, the farmer adds another floor to his house.

Aibono is enabling many such success stories. Aibono hopes to expand its services to more than 500 farmers in the Nilgiris and to parts of Karnataka by end of 2018. As the momentum grows, it will expand to other parts of the country.

The challenge for companies like Aibono and for entrepreneurs like Rajkumar will be to create scalable models. As such entrepreneurs experiment with new ideas, their real success will allow millions of farmers to get access to smart inputs with cloud and AI technology.

*

The Indian agriculture sector has just about begun taking steps to integrate technology into their basic processes. Companies, large and small, are coming up with innovative solutions to ensure efficiency but they will not be able to get a comprehensive view of the sector. The national electronic market is a good step towards bringing technology-enabled transparency in trading. The role of policy makers to enhance infusion of technology remains. A combination of global firms like Cargill, domestic platforms like NCDEX and young start-ups like Aibono can together bring technology to the sector that needs it the most.

10

EDUCATION AND TRAINING

Educomp's Tech Romp

At the border of New Delhi and Gurgaon is a tightly packed cluster of buildings that house companies with diverse interests, from insurance to hospitality to technology. Among them is the headquarters of Educomp, one of the most aggressive start-ups in the Indian education sector that moved with speed to bring tech-fuelled education to primary and high schools.

In a classroom set-up inside the office, chairman and founder Shantanu Prakash proudly demonstrates how teachers use technology-based learning tools for students. Educomp has created 20,000 modules of 3D multimedia content. Teachers use the remote control to display on a digital whiteboard screen the appropriate module for a particular session for a particular class and grade. The module may include slides, videos, and 3D models. With these aids, a teacher can get students to understand complex issues faster. The students are also equipped with tablets loaded with content that corresponds to the module. In a one-and-a-half-minute video, for instance, students can see a 3D model and flow-chart showing how oxygen can be derived from hydrogen peroxide with the help of a catalyst. In the video, the molecules move about, attaching and reattaching themselves to each other. This helps students understand concepts that may appear difficult and makes a subject like chemistry come alive.

Educomp says that 6 million students in private schools and 17.5 million students in government-run schools have used its content. Prakash feels technology will soon be the only way to deliver learning to all ages. He says, 'I think India is actually well prepared to deal with the Fourth Industrial Revolution. I feel confident about India because the young people of India are very receptive to technology. Over the years, Indian schools, Indian students, and Indian universities have demonstrated a very enthusiastic adoption of new knowledge-economy technologies, and therefore the sectors that are seeing the maximum change are those like personalized learning.'

Prakash says one of the challenges students have in India is that their classrooms are too crowded. There can be fifty students in the classroom, and the teacher is fairly mediocre because India as an economy can't really afford to pay teachers high salaries. The result is that the quality of the curriculum and teacher-interaction with the students are also of the lowest quality. This flies in the face of every bit of research on brain development or how the brain learns. It is a well-established fact that students are unique learners and cognitive individuals, and need a personalized learning strategy, which society cannot provide because of the way we organize our educational system.

Therefore, one of the key disruptive technologies that will impact students and schools is going to be personalized learning experience. Prakash sees an emergence of a vast range of tools and technologies to facilitate this. One company that offers them is Fliplearn, a company he works with very closely as a mentor.

Fliplearn is a digital platform that not only provides personalized assessment but also continuously monitors the progress and performance of a child in school by collecting data on the child's attendance, homework, marks and grades scored in school, the posts put up by the child on the platform, and so on. The platform uses artificial intelligence to create a cognitive profile of the student. Based on this profile, Fliplearn works with content partners to provide personalized suggestions for the child's education, based on the learning capabilities of the child.

The other example Prakash shares is from the higher-education industry, where sites like Edx or Coursera have actually been taking centre-stage in terms of democratizing learning. One of the key challenges of education is that so far education was only available at a great cost and great inconvenience, requiring labour mobility across borders, which is obviously not optimal. But websites like Coursera, Udacity, and Edx are changing the game by providing courses from top universities like Stanford to learners across the world. The data suggests that a disproportionately large number of learners on these web portals is actually coming from India.

Prakesh says he recognized very early that digital, social, Internet, and mobile technologies are really the ways to reach out to the country. 'If India is going to be a knowledge economy, then millions of learners will need to be included in the educational system rather than excluded. It's impossible to build the next one million schools that India needs, so you will actually have to put the learning on the cloud. Educomp's research and development are in that direction.' Educomp's Smartclass Pro model is a fully digital online product that provides lessons to students across the country in the language of their choice. Educomp is also betting big on delivering content in vernacular languages instead of restricting itself to just English.

Initiatives like Fliplearn too are making big changes in the area of personalized learning. Going forward Prakash sees students working with smart bands which are able to measure their stress levels, their emotional highs and lows, their sleep, their nutrition, and all the super important parts of the growing-up process. Access to this data will be provided in real-time to stakeholders such as parents or school teachers to enable better decision making.

Fliplearn approaches schooling much the way NIIT and Naukri approach adult education and career planning, respectively – through deep data, machine learning, and algorithms that help create neuro-cognitive profiles of students. The data points range from attendance, scores, curricular and extra-curricular interests, etc. These inputs are processed through evolving algorithms to create profiles for each student. Based on these profiles, individually-tailored content sources are curated and provided to the students.

As the saying goes, if the proof of the pudding is in the eating, Fliplearn is well on its way to proving itself as the next big thing in the field of primary education. Within fifteen months of its launch, it is now processing details of over 2.3 million students at 2,300 schools.

*

A study by Google and KPMG suggests that India's online education market will grow to $1.96 billion and to 9.6 million users by 2021, from $247 million and 1.6 million users in 2016. There are five categories of online and technology-led education. Primary and secondary supplemental education; test preparation; reskilling and online certifications; higher education; and language and casual learning.

Reskilling and online certification is the largest category today, at $93 million. Primary and secondary supplemental education will be the largest category by 2021, at $773 million, with a compounded annual growth rate of 60 per cent. Test preparation will be the fastest growing category, with a CAGR of 64 per cent. Improved Internet penetration, smartphones, a young population, the falling cost of online education, and the government's digital efforts are driving this growth.[1]

The use of technology to teach students will be critical for a country where not only is unemployment high, but unemployability too. But the workspace and job markets are changing so rapidly that education will have to be very agile and responsive to create relevant workforces. For employment, the focus has to be shifted to skills that will make professionals employable. What is referred to as a gig economy is really about self-employment or project-based work. None of this will involve the typical nine-to-five job that was created during the earlier industrial revolution.

For decades, public and private institutions have been developing and promoting policies that increase employment. The concept of employment has been rooted in our minds as a regular nine-to-five job with some perks and benefits. The government-developed policies on this front were inflexible but suited the purpose of the previous decades.

India has grown rapidly in the last twenty-five years. Despite the best efforts of the government, India is currently facing a severe crisis of unemployment. Labour Bureau data shows that unemployed people constitute about 5 per cent of the employable population.[2] A more pressing concern, as recently stated by NITI Aayog's Bibek Debroy, is the rise in unemployability – a direct consequence of education that has failed to equip the population for the demands of the industry. To meet this crisis head-on, a totally new approach may be needed in India. We may have to overcome the models of the past to create an atmosphere in which a rising population of skilled workers is able to earn a livelihood with dignity.

Unemployment is as much a social crisis as an economic one. It is as much a political issue as is the human right to a dignified life. Industry has to be as worried as political leaders about this.

Globally, the debate has moved from creating employment to ensuring work. And not just work but a work culture. While in India we see workers as wearing white or blue collars, a new intermediate class is emerging. This intermediate class includes workers who may be active on shop floors but could be more skilled than many educated engineers. Companies have to prepare for this new class of workers. Old distinctions between white and blue collar workers will become extinct.

As robotics and extreme automation gain traction in India, companies will have to deploy a totally new class and cadre of workers. Previously held concepts and categories of workers will not be relevant. The Indian automotive industry is world class. It would not be long before their workers match the skills of their counterparts in global factories.

The services sector is changing shape too. Job descriptions are evolving faster than organizational structures. In the hospitality industry, the front-desk staff may soon disappear, as they have at many airline check-in counters. People will still be needed, but for tasks that could be more complex and less rigid. The same front-office representative could become a 'customer-delight executive' who ensures '360-degree satisfaction' for a hotel guest.

Even though manufacturing will require higher automation, the services sector has the potential of creating more work than the number of jobs being destroyed. Take agriculture, for instance. Rising mechanization in agriculture will reduce the need for farm labour. However, the logistics and value chain of taking farm products for processing and then to consumers will need millions of trained people. Enabling people with a farm background to be trained for food-related services is the most natural step to take.

IoT is connecting devices, industries, and functions in a way few imagined and at a pace that few can cope with. A Gartner study estimates that more than 13 billion devices in the consumer and enterprise segment will be connected to the Internet.[3]

What will this do to workers? Will it provide them more opportunities or will it irreplaceably remove jobs? It is difficult to predict the impact of such fundamental shifts led by fast-changing technology. Here, the agility of business leaders to create ever-transforming organizations will be important.

What is easy to plan for is change. Flexibility in attitude, policies, and approach will ensure that individuals and institutions adapt rapidly to change. Industry leaders and policy makers have to focus on ensuring that people are prepared for the new types of work that will emerge. Jobs may disappear, but there will always be work to be done. Who will do them? The issues of unemployability could easily lead to the creation of people who just don't know what work they can do even if there are opportunities.

Leaders agree they have to invest in nurturing a new work culture. It is as much about culture as about work. The white collar, professional class is being reorganized into virtual groups who deliver projects and then disband. Such teams come together again with different members for different projects. So the concept of departments and permanent teams may become irrelevant soon. It is happening in avant garde organizations, especially start-ups, and could soon be mainstream in large legacy companies.

Corporate leaders are ready for the change. Millennials don't believe in silos or hierarchy. They are willing to experiment as long as they are productively engaged. This is as much true in rural centres as in urban. The young think alike across domestic and global geographies.

As we debate the future of jobs, we must be prepared for new ideas, technologies, and structures too. Work and culture will matter. Jobs and employment may not.

New types of jobs also require new approaches to education and skilling. Many companies are paying a lot of attention to skilling employees by using internal technology platforms. These platforms allow individuals to up-skill as well as help companies create specific teams for specific tasks.

*

BoTs Train at Skills Alpha

While education and training is important, so is the agility of an individual to reskill while holding a job. A new category of opportunity is emerging, where companies are creating solutions for existing employees who want to reskill.

With many job functions disappearing, employees have to focus on acquiring new skills or upgrading their current skills.

A company that is focusing on this need is the newly launched Skills Alpha, a skills management platform. The young company helps employees get job-ready and also allows them to self-learn for professional development. It connects employees, CEOs, business opportunity managers, and HR heads to ensure that teams are ready for every new opportunity that comes along.

Skills Alpha realized that business cycles have shortened, so where companies used to have two or three years' time to adapt strategies, they now have only twelve to eighteen months. The key differentiator today for any organization is talent, because any other competitive advantage organizations have is easily replicated by rival companies in ten to twelve months. One thing that really sets organizations apart is the talent they are developing.

Skills Alpha developed a platform that allows teams and individuals to constantly upgrade their skills. Traditionally, learning-only programmes take employees away from work and are infrequent too. Often the knowledge gathered becomes dated even before the certificate is issued. A constant learning platform allows for the agility that is essential for evolving needs.

Training and development can also become uni-dimensional, since one usually sees blanket training for everyone without adequate assessment of individual skills and abilities. Through the AI-powered Skills Alpha platform, individuals can assess their levels, choose their skills, and begin to learn. Apart from training, professionals can also seek social learning from peers, coaching and mentoring from experts.

The platform is especially focused on millennial attitudes, understanding that they get restless if their education is not linked to immediate impact. The learning modules are customized based on observations on a person's behaviour, their attention span, and experience. Learning is delivered byte-sized. Consequently, content videos are of no more than two to four minutes. The 'learners' also want to be able to instantly access the information they have learned.

Once an employee logs into Skills Alpha, this is how it progresses.

The employee can see a career path based on aspirations and skill affinity including gap analysis. This helps her identify opportunities within the organization and also helps her understand what type of skilling is required to walk that career path. A skilling BoT on the platform will use natural language processing to guide the employee through her options. The employee can clarify her doubts and identify the steps needed to be taken after conversing with the BoT. Essentially, the Alpha BoT is a personal skilling buddy that uses Deep Learning (a subset of AI) to guide, support and mentor the employee in her career.

Another thing that Skills Alpha does is analyze a lot of the information that comes in through the system in terms of user behaviour, and collate those into actions for different people. The platform generates a real-time skill inventory, so that managers, L&D or resource management teams can easily identify gaps, plan resource allocation or succession planning.

Skills Alpha has already started making inroads into companies with a large Indian IT exporter that is a part of a diversified conglomerate, a leading white good major, a women's micro-enterpreneurship network, and an industry specialist in the hire, train, and deploy segment subscribing to its platform for employee skilling. Several more including an IT industry association cluster for SME firms are expected to sign-up in the coming months.

*

Edutech refers to the application of technology in delivering education, although, as far as application is concerned, it can be expanded to include technology and tech-enabled solutions applied in an educational context. Smart-boards, interactive modules, even closed-loop locators, are some examples of edutech.

While there is no denying that the intent and content of education has evolved rapidly in the past century, the manner in which it is conveyed has often stuck faithfully to the tried and trusted principles of yore. The challenge of delivering, at a minimum, the same standard of experience to as many children, with their myriad interests, aptitudes, and capabilities, as possible has always held education back from embracing radical innovations out of fear that a mistake might be made.

Another major challenge for edutech has been the absence of a panacea, a catch-all solution that can be applied across the board, irrespective of the subject under consideration. Science subjects, for instance, require experimentation and observation; arts, on the other hand, require assimilation and discussion. At higher levels, even the lines between the 'scientific' and the 'artistic' are blurred. In a college teaching advanced science, it is not merely enough to know the how's and the what's; it is equally, or perhaps at times even more, important that the students understand the consequences of, say, experimentation.

Broadly speaking, technology in the sphere of education has been used in two ways – horizontally, that is, to address the problem of reach, and vertically, to enhance the learning experience for those already reached.

While it can be argued that even the earliest distance-education programmes – such as Sir Isaac Pitman's course for shorthand or the University of London's External Programme – were innovative uses of the technology available in those days, it would be more acceptable to claim that technology (as it is accepted now) really made a difference to education only with the emergence of computers, television, and satellites.

In the late '50s and early '60s, the euphoria of the first wave of television programming had died down and in its place was the realization that the medium, which had been largely entertainment-centric until then, could be used for a more meaningful purpose. Many children's programmes were produced, becoming quite popular with their demographic through the use of 'cool' science projects that the audience could replicate at home or through documentaries on faraway lands and practices.

In 1975, NASA and ISRO jointly ran the Satellite Instructional Television Experiment (SITE) to explore the viability of using satellite broadcasting to reach remote regions with educational content. While the experiment did prove the concept, it was later shelved when NASA moved its satellite away from the orbit it needed to be in for the project. This experiment was the precursor to many other attempts across the world.

The development of Optical Mark Recognition was a significant leap that enabled examiners to hold large-scale examinations where the results could be evaluated objectively and quickly, yet inexpensively.

As computers became more mass-market, schools, especially in the West and in Japan, quickly woke up to the possibilities of augmenting learning with multimedia tools. As advancements in computing and rendering power grew manifold, so too did the richness of content. In the mid-'90s, most children were amazed by graphics rendered on black-and-white screens. By the year 2000, colour screens were the norm, and a few years later, 'lifelike' colour was the in-thing. Nowadays, tablets or handheld PCs with touchscreens, virtual reality goggles, and interactive smart-boards have redefined the minimum standards expected of a techno-savvy classroom.

Across the world, bandwidth speeds have grown consistently in the past two decades. In the confluence of cheaper access to the Internet, compact devices, and wireless connectivity, education has been one of the biggest gainers. It is now possible for a student sitting in a remote village in UK's Yorkshire, for example, to follow the live telecast of an experiment being carried out at Stanford or MIT.

One of the most significant developments in this space recently has been the emergence of services like Coursera, which has tied up with some of the leading universities across the globe to offer a variety of certificate courses.

Combining audio-visual resources with assignments the student has to complete, such ventures have attempted to take the question of distance and physical presence completely out of the education picture.

In India, in addition to SITE (1975-76), many other attempts were made to take education to the masses and the remote regions of the country. However, in the absence of proper equipment, training, and checks and balances, these attempts were either abandoned halfway through or failed to meet the ambitious expectations they started out with. Between 1970 and 1995, caught between runaway technology costs and internal crises of one sort or the other, education suffered.

For a long while, therefore, an immersive learning environment in schools stood for the teacher passing out a hard-bound book that had colour pictures. Multimedia presentations meant overhead projectors and transparency sheets; but printed materials were usually the only source of information.

All this has changed in the past two decades, coinciding with the increasing affordability of personal computers and availability of digital content. The first phase of this revolution was the adoption of discs with videos, containing animations and presentations. The second phase was marked by the increased penetration of Internet in homes and schools, affecting the demand for hard content (books, CDs, DVDs) and supplanting them with on-demand sources online.

The third wave – in terms of experiential learning – is happening right now. Schools are adopting smart solutions for their classrooms. These 'smart' solutions, driven by domestic pioneers such as Educomp and Tata's Edge, have started altering the way knowledge is exchanged in classrooms, creating an environment where the teacher is more of a facilitator than an instructor.

Typically, such a solution involves smart-boards on which specially created content can be projected and which the students can manipulate with touch. With the government promoting the start-up ecosystem in the country, as many as 500 start-ups are currently working in this space. While investments are few and far between, unlike the feeding frenzy one associates with e-com ventures, there is still a lot of interest from venture capitalists. Given that the paying customer – a parent, or a school – is often not the end-user (a student), companies are finding it difficult to press their value propositions.

One thread, however, unites most of these start-ups. Whether it is resource management, content delivery or even interactive exchange, most of these start-ups are betting on mobile phones as the preferred delivery mode. Even virtual reality, once a complex proposition that required powerful computers and expensive set-ups, can now be harnessed through apps and specially-made (but budget-friendly) goggles.

For a while in the recent past, Massive Open Online Courses – or MOOCs, as they are known within the industry – became extremely popular before ceding ground to the next wave of bite-size, customized learning. MOOC, as the expansion suggests, represented courses that were taught online, through webinars, video interactions, etc., for a larger audience than would have been possible in a typical classroom set-up. *The New York Times* went so far as to call 2012 the year of MOOCs.

Variants, naturally, emerged as organizers went about the task of popularizing their offerings. Coursera, Khan Academy, and Udemy were some of the early, and prominent, players in this field. They offered paid and free courses, with the paid courses often including a certificate of merit/completion from the University or institution actually conducting that course. It was not that the service providers needed to arrange the content themselves – they simply created their own platforms where tutors and learners could come together. Harvard, Princeton, Stanford, MIT, Caltech – all the prestigious institutions of the world could be found on one MOOC platform or the other.

*

Jobs by Algorithm at Naukri

From skilling to finding new jobs is not a big distance. Searching for a job is now easier, thanks to the many portals that specialize in it. But even this job search industry is using artificial intelligence and other tools to create the perfect match between employers and employees. While there are many companies assisting in placement/hiring of human resources, there is not much that separates them from each other once you move past their operational tactics. At the end of the day, they use their databases of supply and demand to match job-seekers and recruiters. They may employ technological tools in different ways, but still depend on manual intervention at the end of the day to come up with the 'best fits'.

On the face of it, Naukri.com is no different from the others in the industry. While it is the market leader in India, with traffic share currently at 76 per cent (measured by Comscore) and over 50 million registered profiles, it is still a platform that connects job-seekers with recruiters. But unlike the other manpower service firms, Naukri began investing in machine learning and artificial intelligence more than a decade ago. Recommended jobs for job-seekers yielded very strong results at an early stage. Collaborative filtering techniques were deployed for 'those who applied to job A and had also applied to other jobs'. It was an instant hit. Similar algorithms deployed for recruiters, for 'those who viewed a CV and also viewed other CVs', also worked very well.

A large proportion of these registered members receives a job alert every alternate day or on a weekly basis. Job alerts only contain freshly posted jobs on Naukri.com in the last two/three days. It is probably the main reason why Naukri Job Alerts have one of the highest open-and-click-through rates. Yet job-seekers complained about the relevance of jobs they were alerted about. That was identified as one of the important problems to address in early 2010.

In 2010-11, Naukri started analysing the relevance of job recommendations that it was sending out to the candidates. However, a pure parametric approach along with keyword search was not yielding results, and dissatisfaction was very high. Naukri built a topic-based matching algorithm which helped it match the job-seeker profile with jobs in another dimension than just keywords. In addition, Naukri introduced several higher-level features like providing for a job-seeker's function/department, industry, and role, which were based on job-seeker behaviour. This evolution was called Machine Learning 1.0 for Naukri.com.

Machine Learning 1.0 for Naukri.com

The process of improving the job alerts was an incremental one. Naukri built the logic step-by-step, and with every incremental step its understanding of the relevant problem improved.

Discovery of 'Role' – 'Role' is the most critical variable. A deep dive into behavioural data showed several interesting patterns. Job-seekers were not sticking to their Functional Areas (departments) and were applying across Functional Areas.

a. The pattern of application clearly indicated that Role was more important than Functional Area/department.
b. Very similar Roles were present in multiple Functional Areas. For example, the sales Role existed in industry-specific Functional Areas. GM Accounts existed in Accounts Functional Areas as well as in the Top Management Functional Area. Also, several Functional Areas were very close, for example, Accounts and Banking.

Limitation of Keyword search – Key Skills entered by job-seekers represent what they consider as important. Logically, a search on Jobs should use the Key Skills entered by the job-seeker. However, some of the job-seekers had not entered their Key Skills. A large gap existed in the Key Skills entered and their skills as apparent from the CVs. Naukri needed a robust mechanism which did not fail because of data inadequacy.

Handling of Categorical Variables – When Naukri compared two jobs and their relevance to the job-seeker, attributes like 'Role' were important. The key challenge was to translate this into a distance function that can be used for predicting relevance for the job-seeker. Similarly, attributes like Industry or Location required identification of a good distance function.

Job-seeker Resume – A match between a job-seeker's expertise and the requirements from the recruiter is essentially a match between the CV/resume and the Job Description. Of course, there are challenges – if a CV is old or a Job Description is incomplete, this may not work very well. Yet, Naukri needed a mechanism for matching the candidate CV and the Job Description.

Apply Behaviour – It is very much possible that apply behaviour of a job-seeker will deviate from the CV/resume. Apply behaviour can provide insight into the aspirations of the job-seekers as well as help identify classification errors. Incorporating apply behaviour in identifying matching jobs for job-seekers is another significant challenge.

By studying these variables and changing its algorithms, not only did Naukri manage to improve the relevance of jobs it was sending to seekers, it also managed to reduce the computation time of the alert. Parallel techniques with multi-threading approaches helped deliver better results in less than 20 per cent of the time. Naukri also started measuring the satisfaction of candidates with its recommendations. This, opposed to the number of applications filed through them, would eventually become the benchmark for its success.

Machine Learning 2.0 for Naukri.com

While Naukri managed to move beyond keywords to relevant topics, it struggled with the notion of the context in which these topics appeared. For example, these were some of the challenges it faced:

- A Dentist being offered Construction Engineer jobs – This complaint came from a dentist working in a civil hospital of the Indian Army in one of the north-eastern states. She was getting 'construction engineer' jobs, and obviously they were irrelevant to her profile. An investigation revealed that she had mentioned terms like 'civil hospital', 'constructing the teeth', 'root canal', 'cementing the teeth', etc. The algorithm was picking these terms and matching them against construction jobs.
- Machine-Learning Scientist getting Vegetable Breeder jobs – Another complaint came from a machine-learning expert who got 'vegetable breeder' jobs. When Naukri analysed the job, the job contained skills like statistical analysis of multiple genes, evolution of species, etc., which matched with the candidate's skill sets. Again, the algorithm was missing the context while matching skills.

The interesting challenge of context was solved when Naukri.com acquired MakeSense Technologies, a two-person machine-learning team that had built a search system based on a library of designations, skills, and inter-relationships among them. As Naukri incorporated these inter-relationships, it managed to partially solve the context in which the matching happened.

In addition to applying this, Naukri also introduced a mechanism to rate the job-seeker applying against a job. Recruiters tend to get a lot of applications, and some of them are highly irrelevant.

Machine Learning 4.0 for Naukri.com

As Naukri got a deeper understanding of jobs and job-seekers, it built several enabling elements like CV Parser, libraries of skills, designations, and companies. In addition, it explored newer technologies like neural networks and deep-learning algorithms.

The Naukri analytics team identified the above challenges and incrementally solved them in association with the product team and the technology team. And, of course, they noticed a major improvement in relevance feedback from job-seekers throughout their journey in the last seven years.

Hiring the best data scientists has been a constant challenge. While the reputation of the company helps, the talent is still lacking. Over the next few years, Naukri plans to invest in even more machine-learning techniques to fine-tune the search to match the right job to the right person.

*

Data Analytics Fuels NIIT

The earliest of technology training companies in India, NIIT brought the use of computers to many a home and many an individual. When it began in 1982, NIIT opened a chain of training centres across the country to help people with non-technical skills to become comfortable with using computers. In those days, computerization was considered as high-tech and futuristic as bionic body parts are today. Since then NIIT has expanded to offer training and education for individuals and institutions.

Now NIIT has several diverse operations, including a higher-education initiative with NIIT University in Rajasthan.

In keeping with the current technology trends, NIIT now uses its data science platform and strategies for data analytics to generate insights and to enable fact-based decision making. These technologies have been deployed and implemented for NIIT's own business operations and the 'Learning and Talent' group of its corporate customers.

The data-driven insights are of two categories – learner insights, and business insights.

These insights can be further grouped into descriptive (data points that suggest what has happened) and predictive (data points that suggest what could happen or provide guidance to what possibly should happen).

The learner insights provide information related to learning effectiveness and behaviour such as time spent, completion status, scores, and usage patterns of the learner across the learning path. All this usage data is crunched to create actionable insights that help intervention.

For example, how popular and helpful are discussion threads and resources? One can also identify how videos or any learning material are consumed, how many times they were replayed, paused or completed, etc. One can also see what content and formats resonate most with learners, and then use all of these insights to determine how the next training module must be designed.

The technology also identifies patterns of behaviour – for example, the correlation between people who take excellent notes or browse through supplementary content and the scores they obtain – to derive meaningful insights. These insights can be used to identify possible learners at risk or to identify patterns that improve learning.

NIIT is building prediction engines that will make use of 'patterns of behaviour' and dynamically create personalized learning paths to help learners succeed and achieve the desired outcome.

The business insights provide in-depth learning analytics to business sponsors and provide a big-picture view of the learning ecosystem to enable informed decisions. This includes business metrics delivered in an easy-to-comprehend manner to help key stakeholders make better-informed decisions during the entire lifecycle of training and related services.

To generate these insights, huge data from multiple systems are combined into a single middleware before it is mined. The nature of the data and the insights generated depend on the business needs. Some of the examples of metrics generated for different businesses include:

NIIT Retail B2C

- Lead Generation Analysis – provides various cuts/ dimensions and real-time comparisons across dimensions.
- Lead Conversion Analysis – provides insights into the type of leads that convert, to help analysis and make informed decisions on forthcoming campaigns.
- Popular courses – by usage, by enrolments, coupled with demographic information.

- Plotting the probability of leads that have high chance of conversion. This helps the marketing team target high-potential customers and convert them to enrol for a course.

Technology Framework

The technology (data science platform) framework consists of tools/engines under three broad categories:

Data collectors: The tools/components under this category act as data creator or data aggregator. To capture learner behaviour, all clicks/interactions with the digital learning material (both offline and online) made by the learner in the learning environment is captured real-time. NIIT silently records interactions without hampering the actual learning experience. In a similar way, for business systems, the data aggregator pulls data from across various systems e.g. Learning Management Systems, Procurement Systems, Performance Management, Learning Content Design and Development related toolsets, and more. This results in a huge data set which accumulates into the data collector over a period of time.

Data processors: The tools/components under this category apply statistical techniques to summarize the data for reporting. Some of the data produced here is put back in summarized form into the collector for further processing. The data processors include algorithm engines that create models for predictive analysis. These models are regularly trained with a new set of data for continuous improvement of prediction/ recommendations.

Data visualizers: The tools/components under this category provide interactive visual representations of data and also provide filters, comparisons, and visualization of the data, thereby aiding decision making.

*

Education has adapted rapidly to technology in recent years. The momentum will increase, but the real challenge will be to scale in time to meet India's needs. Building sustainable business models that can generate revenue to deploy technology will decide how rapid the scale-up will be.

11

ENERGY: OLD AND NEW

Robotics Fans Havells' Future

Few companies can claim to invest in technology a sum equal to its annual profits. While some may come close today, very few did it in the 1980s. Home-grown Havells was founded by the late Qimat Rai Gupta when he bought the brand from a failing company in 1971. QRG invested in manufacturing electrical products, and over time built a $1.4 billion company. 'If I look back, we bought our first computer in 1982, and ours was the third computer in New Delhi. We bought it for 6.35 lakh rupees while our entire year's profit was 6.4 lakh rupees,' says QRG's son and current chairman of Havells, Anil Rai Gupta.

'Since then, technology has been the key enabler for transformation at Havells. The company has always been a firm believer in the use of technology because it opens new vistas of growth and opportunity. We believe in constantly innovating, ideating, and tackling challenges to break new ground in technology. This work ethic and belief has given us a definite edge over our competitors,' Anil says.

Today at Havells, robotics, IoT, and artificial-intelligence-based technologies are driving change in various functions. These technologies are very important for Havells. For instance, it has applications like the mobile catalogue. A potential consumer can take a picture of a room and, using the app, can put up a product like a fan to see how it will look in the room when it is installed. 'We're going to use big data in IoT, and we are using robotics today in our manufacturing units. We are getting data on the performance of machines to see how we can reduce the breakdown rate or increase the efficiency of a machine. We are looking at 3D printing soon and are definitely at the forefront of using these technologies,' Anil says.

Havells has been investing in upgrading its plants for the last seven to eight years. The company says it is examining ways to reduce the rate of defects on the line and project it on dashboards so that products can be monitored for defects and changed in real- time. 'Even today, we use SCADA (supervisory control and data acquisition), and if there is a fault in the machine, the downtime is reduced because an alarm goes off immediately. To take this forward, we will aggregate data and check machines which are breaking down and reduce downtime,' Anil says.

Energy, or to be more precise, electrical energy, has and will always be a key input for industry, irrespective of every other factor in their input mix. The quest for a more efficient source of energy, therefore, has always existed, pushing the boundaries of the day and age, questioning all conventional norms in its bid.

Initially, power plants were highly localized – servicing a property or a production house, or a small geographical region – and were either water- or steam-powered. Output was low, transmission losses were high, and the industry was still divided between direct current and alternating current. Later on, massive hydro-electric dams were built. However, there was limited scope for expansion of such projects, what with their massive impact on the ecology and local population, not to mention the geographical instability they create due to the weight of water on the underlying soil.

Nuclear power generation was commercially introduced in 1954 with the power plant in Obninsk, Russia. It generated around 5MW of power – to put it in perspective, Mumbai alone required 4GW of energy in 2015. It was expected to be a more efficient energy solution, but the Three Mile Island accident (1979) and the Chernobyl tragedy (1986) drove home the risks of this technology. The Fukushima disaster of 2011 has all but signalled the end of nuclear power generation – the world cannot afford the fallout from yet another incident of this nature.

Since the late 1980s, there has also been a determined push towards eco-friendly or renewable energy sources such as wind, tidal power, and solar power. For a while, it seemed as if these sources would be less economically viable than thermal or nuclear power plants. But with depleting fuel supply (for thermal production) and the increased cost of mitigating risks (for nuclear production), that's no longer the case. With many NGOs and even private individuals investing in green sources of power, they are now the energy industry's favoured children.

But it is not just power generation where the money is pouring in. The power industry loses anywhere from 4 per cent to 10 per cent of its generation in transmission losses, theft, improper loading, and other inefficiencies that still plague the system. This is what the next wave of innovators is striking at.

Utility companies are employing networked sensors at different points of the cycle – at the generation end (for safety – to monitor pressure, voltage, temperature, etc.), at the nodes on the transmission side (to measure voltage, current, wind speeds, and detect thefts between terminals), at transformers (for stepping up or down voltages), and at end-user points (with meters that measure not only consumption but its profile too, such as the load factor, quality of network, usage against time, etc.).

User-end monitoring has been enabled particularly because of the new-found interest in IoT. Consumer industries prefer the term 'big data', but the power industry might go with 'huge data' instead, given the volume of data that it wants to collect and process. The idea isn't just to know what is happening in real-time, but also to retrieve enough data so as to be able to predict future loads and requirements so that distribution can be redirected as needed.

Besides, companies and even 'smart homes' are now employing IoT solutions to manage their energy requirements. For instance, there are now sensors that can detect the population density of offices and adjust the lighting or air-conditioning accordingly; there are cloud-based services that allow one to control heaters, refrigerators, entertainment units, air-conditioning units, security systems at homes and small offices or even to automate their use.

In 1902, the first power station in India was set up at Sivanasamudram in what was then Mysore state, with a production limit of 4.5 MW. Today, in just over a century, the country has an installed capacity of over 315 GW (Feb 2017). Coal still accounts for almost 60 per cent of the power, followed by hydel (16 per cent) and wind (9 per cent)

Almost till the end of the 1990s, power generation suffered because of a variety of factors – focus on expansion instead of efficiency, unavailability of high-quality transmission cables, engineering issues, theft, and populist measures that affected the sustainability of these projects. With almost negligible private-sector involvement (except in the supply of equipment, itself a restricted process due to economic sanctions and an inability to purchase) there was no incentive for the sector to be efficient. Power thefts on a large scale, especially in the rural areas, were often excused by the state governments themselves for political reasons.

However, in recent years, after putting in place a national grid and allowing private players to get into distribution, the sector has seen a sea change in efficiency, if not in cost control. In fact, Tamil Nadu and Gujarat were among the first states to allow private firms to set up and operate power generation stations and sell their excess power to the state. In Kanyakumari district in southern Tamil Nadu, the National Highway winds through a windmill farm that stretches on into the horizon on both sides.

While there is a concerted drive to make power generation more efficient and eco-friendly, the thrust in India has been primarily on the consumption side. With an increasingly urban, connected population, and higher per-capita consumption, the Indian demographic is perhaps the right size for IoT solutions providers to tap. Companies like Godrej and Philips are offering networked homes, where energy consumption can be controlled remotely or even automatically. Thus, for instance, a coffee-maker can be switched on as you pull into your driveway, bringing it to the right temperature just as you enter, reducing the need to leave it on or having to monitor it yourself.

Companies like Havells that make energy consuming products or those that produce energy themselves have found IoT very useful. Not just that, for power generators there is a long list of activities that are being automated, mechanized, and monitored using drones and sensors.

*

Tata Power's AdoRE

Tata power is also pretty well invested in new technologies.

'ADoRE' (ADvanced-centre for Diagnostics & Reliability Enhancement) for the Tata Power assets in its generating stations has been set up at the corporate level in CTDS Noida. ADoRE has the following mission objectives:

a) To continuously monitor the health and performance of critical power plant equipment across the fleet of power stations in Tata Power.
b) To assess equipment operating conditions to minimize operational risks of unacceptable schedule interruptions or increased maintenance.
c) To bring in early identification and advance warnings of incipient failure modes, and impending equipment problems to avoid forced outages and catastrophic failure.

d) To identify subtle changes in system and equipment behaviour based on real-time data, present trends, and historical data.
e) To use state-of-the-art analytics, algorithms, pattern-recognition, and decision-making tools, together with performance-assessment tools, gap analysis, and cause-effect scenarios for diagnostics and reliability enhancement.
f) To provide the generating stations with expert advice on equipment performance-health scenarios and operating regime changes towards optimal asset lifecycle management.

The ADoRE infrastructure and assets comprise a state-of-the-art control room set-up of IT hardware and analytic software, and high-speed communication links with all Tata Power generating stations for capture of critical real-time data. A pool of expert equipment analysts and power plant engineers are interfacing with the station O&M teams for achieving the ADoRE mission objectives. ADoRE is fully operational for the company's thermal units at Mundra, Maithon and Trombay, and is expected to extend its diagnostics and coverage, aligned to its mission objectives, to units in Jojobera and Haldia in the next one year. Once the Renewables Centralized SCADA control room is set up at PSCC Trombay, ADoRE is scheduled to extend its coverage to its renewables units, i.e., its wind, solar, and hydro plants.

Asset health monitoring often comprises fixed alarm limits defined within control systems, smart devices, and SCADA. Additionally, fixed end-of-life and equipment runtime calculation are used for determining an asset's health. It is a daunting task to identify and maintain fixed limits and calculations that can vary based on the actual device characteristics, operating history, ambient conditions, equipment conditions, and device settings.

ADoRE, therefore, comprises an advanced software, PRiSMR, which uses Advanced Pattern Recognition (APR) Technique to predict the desirable values of each parameter modelled and detects anomalies that are outside the normal expected pattern.

The entire diagnostics is based on models that are created for each of the critical plant equipment. For a typical coal-based 500 MW unit, about 200 such models covers all critical equipment in a unit, like reliability models for turbines, fans, pumps, heaters, etc.; performance models for turbine efficiency, heat rate, etc.; systems models like condensate system, feed water systems, furnace draft systems; and transient models as for turbine start-up, boiler start-up, etc.

The models help simulate different situations and create alerts and alarms. The engineers can thus anticipate problems and prepare a plan to resolve them.

Global Experience and Approach Taken by Utilities Abroad

Fleet-wide monitoring involving predictive analytic software has already been implemented in various utilities in the USA, where diagnostics are being carried out at tier-two remote diagnostics/monitoring centres. Such centres are located within the geographic supply territories or even outside, to some extent, in other countries. One such centre monitoring over fifty to sixty thermal power plants in the US has been set up in Pune, India.

The concept has gained a lot of significance due to the potential benefits of advance warning of impending failures, the economics of centralized monitoring compared with individual monitoring locations, comparative monitoring of similar units and equipment across the fleet, knowledge capture and collaborative exchange for enhanced plant reliability, and predictive maintenance actions.

The predictive analytic software implemented at Tata's centralized fleet-monitoring centre enables plant engineers to take predictive, proactive, risk-informed, and timely decisions. The solution delivers dynamic insight and deep-dive diagnostics for potential behaviour change of the equipment. In several cases across industry, the solution has successfully identified various plant anomalies at an incipient stage and helped plant engineers take timely mitigating actions before the anomalies lead to catastrophic failure or loss of production. This has resulted in significant savings and availability improvements while increasing equipment health visibility and optimizing the logistics of maintenance.

Implementation Approach/Experience at Tata Power

A dedicated control room has been set up for ADoRE at Tata Power Noida in the Core Technology and Diagnostics division of Tata Power. The centre is functional 24x7 since August 2014.

The ADoRE server, which uses PRiSM® application for diagnostic functionalities, interfaces with the PI data/servers of operating plants which fetch real-time and historian data to develop/train the models. With the operationalization of

ADoRE, all such diagnostics functionalities have been extended to ten thermal units at Mundra (five), Trombay (three), and Maithon (two).

The functionalities of ADoRE are now poised for scale-up to provide such services to other stations too. The advantages a station is likely to get would consist of advance notifications to avert possible trouble and trip-outs for plant and equipment much before the actual alarm is generated in the site control room. Even a single plant trip thus averted amounts to huge potential cost savings and impacts the plant's operational KPIs in terms of reduction in forced outages. It also enhances plant reliability by providing it enough time for planned maintenance tasks to avert impending failures.

New Sources

Given the twin objectives of sustainable development and energy security, the Indian government embarked on an ambitious goal of adding 100GW of solar power and 75GW of wind energy to the Indian grid by the year 2022. Additionally, in the COP-21 meet in Paris, a historic accord was reached between member nations to cap their emission targets as a direct response to mitigate the impact of global warming. India was one of the countries that took a leading position in the talks by agreeing to lower its emissions by the year 2030 by 33 per cent to 35 per cent of the 2005 levels. As part of this overarching goal, India has targeted to have 40 per cent of its electricity generation capacity from renewable energy sources.

Current Scenario

Bolstered by the growth in demand of renewable energy that the India market has witnessed over the past five years, and backed by some key policy and regulatory initiatives, solar energy tariff has dropped to ₹3.33/kwh and wind energy tariff to ₹3.46/kwh in the recently conducted capacity auctions in February 2017. These electricity tariffs are lower than base-load coal-generation tariffs, considering that the cost of renewable energy for a given project would remain fixed for twenty-five years. This augurs well for the overall renewable programme, as lower tariffs imply more affordable energy costs, which will directly increase demand for renewable energy over other sources.

Constraints

The availability of solar and wind energy is largely determined by the prevailing weather conditions and therefore characterized by strong variability. Consequently, power generation from these sources cannot easily be matched to the electricity demand as power generated by conventional plants is. This introduces new challenges not only for the operation of single wind and solar power plants, but, with the expected integration of large shares of fluctuating renewable energy, it will also have important consequences for the organization, structure, and management at all levels of the electricity supply system.

Accurate forecasts of renewable power production, therefore, are an essential factor for the successful integration of large amounts of renewable power into the electricity supply system. They must aim to supply precise information on the timing and magnitude of power generation from these variable sources.

The Solution for India

Generally, wind and solar power forecasts derive future power generation numbers using either numerical weather prediction models or statistical approaches, and more often than not relying on both. Any wind or solar power forecast which is produced for time scales of more than several hours is based on the results of Numerical Weather Prediction (NWP). The NWP model is basically a computer simulation of the earth's atmosphere. All the earth's processes, including the ones on the land surface and in the oceans, will affect the weather. By knowing the current state of the atmosphere (i.e., the weather conditions), future changes in the weather are predicted by the model. NWP is based on a set of mathematical equations which describe all of the relevant atmospheric processes.

For solar power generation, depending on the application and its corresponding time scale, different forecasting approaches have been specifically introduced. Time series models using on-site measurements are adequate for the very short-term time scale (ranging from a few minutes up to a few hours). Intra-hour forecasts with a high spatial and temporal resolution may be obtained from ground-based sky imagers. Forecasts based on cloud motion vectors from satellite images show good performance for a temporal range of 30 minutes to 6 hours. Grid integration of PV power mainly requires forecasts for two days ahead or even beyond. These forecasts are based on NWP models.

In view of the proposed plan to have 40 per cent of India's power generation from renewable resources by the year 2030, the central government has planned to develop and deploy Renewable Energy Management Centres (REMC). These REMC would be equipped with state-of-the-art analytics-based forecasting tools, facilities for real-time tracking of renewable energy generation, geo-spatial visualization of renewables generation, and smart software to optimally dispatch the renewable energy into the grid by integrating the REMC with the State Load Dispatch Centres (SLDC) and Regional Load Dispatch Centres (RLDC) that currently manage real-time control of the generation and load balance in each of the states and regions in India.

*

Predictive Maintenance at First Solar

The growing renewable sector has the freedom to adopt new ways of producing and maintaining its energy generation. First Solar has been using data analytics in a very productive way in India. A US-based maker of photovoltaic thin films, First Solar, counts India as its biggest market outside its home country.

First Solar's main focus is on analytics, its CEO in India, Sujoy Ghosh, says. The key objectives for First solar are:

a) Estimating and predicting the weather for 25 years at a given location to determine if the site is good for installing solar plants: This is true for wind plants also. All of the renewable energy industry uses analytics for predicting weather patterns and their impact on the renewable energy generation potential for a given location.

b) Using analytics to operate and maintain solar plants: Specifically, software modelling is used to predict equipment performance and potential failures (in devices like solar panels, transformers, etc.). By using analytic tools, predictive maintenance is conducted. This minimizes plant/equipment downtime as a consequence of a catastrophic failure.
c) Using robotics: In the solar industry internationally, robotics are being deployed (early stage) for cleaning of panels on large solar projects without water. Some companies have started to offer these solutions in India, but the low cost of labour acts as a barrier to entry for these applications.

The use of robots for cleaning solar energy panels is critical. Its slow adoption has begun in India. Israel's Ecoppia has partnered with US-based Sanmina to manufacture robots for the solar industry in India. 'With the rapid growth of the solar industry in India, Ecoppia has seen skyrocketing demand for its E4 technology. The paradigm-shifting technology can clean an entire solar site in just a few hours, keeping solar energy production at peak efficiency,' the company says. The E4 robot is a smart, sensor-enabled, Internet-connected maintenance machine. Its sensors collect weather data and initiate cleaning based on weather conditions. The robot works on the ML format by creating its own schedule. Effectively, the robot is available at the site 99 per cent of the time.

In India, companies like NTPC and Adani Power are among the users of these robots.

*

Avaada: Analytics of Renewable Energy

Every day, every moment, the world around us is changing. We are experiencing unprecedented climatic disruptions. Relentless consumption of natural resources is adversely affecting the environment. 'Globally, weather-related losses and damage have risen,' says Jim Yong Kim, president of the World Bank Group. United Nations Office for Disaster Risk Reduction (UNISDR) had estimated that the true figure of disaster losses – including earthquakes and tsunamis – is between US$250 billion and US$300 billion annually.

Global growth so far has been fuelled by carbon-based energy projects. The energy generated might be considered cost-effective. However, continued usage of this energy will endanger the environment and, consequently, our health.

The leading question is – how can economic prosperity be balanced with environmental sustainability? Shifting to sustainable infrastructure is now the widely accepted tenet. Renewable energy is the key to solving the world's energy-related issues – energy security and climate change arising from increasing consumption of fossil fuels.

Avaada is a renewable energy company working to create a sustainable future for the benefit of the environment and communities. Recognizing that India is at the crossroads of development, it has nurtured a socially inclusive development dream. The efforts are concentrated towards ensuring the sustainability of the power-planet-people nexus. As one of the newer and fast-growing companies in India, it carries the responsibility of bringing about a low-carbon transition in the energy sector.

Avaada believes that economic prosperity in the long term is tied up with the business' responsibility for ecological sustainability and its upholding of social interests. These aspects must be integrated into the business' strategy and corporate decision-making processes.

By combining disruptive technologies and impeccable project execution, it helps make clean energy affordable and accessible.

Within a short span of time, Avaada's team of specialists has pioneered solar power solutions, both in terms of plant size and total installed capacity. Its team was the first to build India's largest portfolio of solar power projects, aggregating to nearly 1 GW in capacity.

Solar and wind power projects are highly sensitive to environmental and climatic conditions. If there is even a slight differential in the conditions – climatic or system-oriented – the quantum of energy generated can take a significant downturn.

For Avaada, building complex solar and wind projects across diverse geographies is the main objective. These projects have been accredited and certified by international organizations in the past. Armed with robust technical know-how and industry experience, Avaada has ensured that each project that is conceptualized, built, and operated, has set benchmarks in project management and optimal plant performance.

The projects that have been built had also set benchmarks within their respective state territories because of their scale. For instance, the 151MW (DC) Neemuch power plant was one of the world's largest solar power plants at the time of its commissioning in 2013. The 302MW Tamil Nadu solar project was the state's largest solar power plant when commissioned last year.

The total generation from solar and wind plants that Avaada had built was 1.652 billion units, as of December 2015, and as a consequence to this, nearly 14,41,100 tonnes of CO_2 emissions were offset.

With its presence across ten states in India, Avaada is working with them to achieve their green targets. The renewable energy projects are located across diverse geographic conditions, ranging from hilly terrain in Karnataka to the plains of Tamil Nadu and Punjab. One of the largest solar power plants that was built by Avaada is located in the rocky environs of Madhya Pradesh. Almost all of these projects are built at some distance from human settlements.

One of the key steps in the project development cycle was the identification and assessment of, and collaboration with, leading technology, plant design, and engineering trendsetters. One such strategic partner with whom Avaada co-developed IoT solutions for renewable energy projects is iPLON.

Given that renewable industry is still in its early growth phase, Avaada needed a solution that could monitor and manage the entire portfolio of its projects in real-time. The solution had to be customized to Indian conditions too. This is where the partnership with iPLON came in. Specialists from both organizations jointly worked to develop a robust architecture that could manage the projects in real-time as well as generate the necessary information required for continuous improvement in plant performance.

iPLON's IoT system comprises three state-of-the-art tools which have efficiently managed operations and maintenance of the power projects. They are:

- iPLON Distributed Data-Centre Technology (iDDC)
- iSolar_Kontrol (iPLON on-site monitoring system)
- iPLON Magic Box for Grid Stability solutions

Renewable energy projects, including solar, require significant capital infusion. It is therefore imperative that they function seamlessly for efficient energy generation.

The power plants that have been built are situated in diverse geographic conditions, as described earlier. In the traditional Indian scenario, operators would be employed to manually look after the operation and maintenance of individual projects. This method requires significant resource and time utilization, and the ensuing costs would accelerate exponentially. Moreover, the data generated is localized and cannot be analysed in real-time to identify performance trends and their respective causes.

By installing the customized automated monitoring system, Avaada is able to prevent instances of system failure and detect any discrepancies or issues much earlier, thereby, ensuring optimal generation. This is a major cost saver for the organization and ensures that revenues are not affected adversely.

With the data collected through the IoT system, Avaada's Operations and Maintenance (O&M) function could also centrally analyse and cross-reference data from various plants to further understand how the system is responding to different environmental conditions as well as to system calibrations (inverters, etc.).

Through an analysis conducted by the O&M function over the years, the actual Peak Load Factor (PLF) achieved by projects is consistently much higher than was anticipated during the design phase. This is due to multiple factors –

engineering efficiency, using tier-one power equipment, and successful implementation and management of the automated monitoring mechanism.

As much as possible, best practices and innovations have been implemented in each subsequent project. For instance, the construction cycle for projects has been decreasing consistently. Using the data collected by the IoT system, Avaada's engineers could analyse the performance of each project with reference to the system installed. Consequent to this, improvements were made in project engineering and design. This has proved beneficial, given that solar technology in India is not as yet established, so there aren't prescribed best practices, unlike the situation in more mature markets like Germany.

The scope for new technology in the energy sector is higher in renewables. The traditional energy generation and distribution companies have to overcome the investment in existing technologies before they adopt new ones.

ACKNOWLEDGEMENTS

In over twenty-five years of writing, reporting, and hosting shows on economic change in India and the world, I considered writing a book a few times but couldn't muster courage. I was daunted by the task and didn't think I had the patience for it.

The theme of Fourth Industrial Revolution grew slowly in me between 2015 and 2016. I participated in and heard many enlightening debates on the subject at various sessions at the World Economic Forum meets in Davos, Delhi and even at Medellin, Colombia.

The theme came to life for me when I interviewed the founder of the World Economic Forum, Prof. Klaus Schwab, at Delhi in 2015. He said India must not only embrace the revolution but also prepare for it. The book on the subject written by Prof. Schwab, launched in 2016, helped me appreciate the impact such a revolution could have for an emerging economy like India. I met and discussed the subject with experts at the annual meeting of the World Economic Forum in Davos in January

2016. By then the topic had begun to move from the fringes to the mainstream, thanks to Prof. Schwab's book.

I noticed that most conversations and examples of the Fourth Industrial Revolution were about the changes taking place in Europe and the US. There was little information about how India was coping or reacting. But then I found a few articles in the media, and had some conversations that led me to think that India had taken to these technologies more than what was apparent.

To test my ideas, I turned to Suman Bose in 2016, the then CEO of Siemens Industry Software and now Executive Partner at private equity firm Lumis Partners. I had met Suman a couple of years earlier in October 2014 at the Global Investors Summit in Indore when Siemens had invited me to chair a session of Industrie 4.0, the German initiative on Internet of Things. The subject was alien and theoretical to most in the audience. It was new to me too, but I warmed up to it.

A few months later, I met Suman over a couple of frugal breakfast sessions at his office in Gurgaon. The peripatetic Suman reached office at 7 a.m. to ensure there was time for uninterrupted brainstorming. My conversations with him confirmed the idea of the book. He told me emphatically that companies had indeed begun investing in such technologies. I have to thank Suman for helping confirm my theory and encouraging me to jump into the project.

I then turned to my friend Mini Kapoor for an introduction to Kanishka Gupta, the intrepid literary agent, whose energy is infectious and exhausting at the same time. He leapt at my idea in just one meeting and efficiently sharpened my book proposal. He chaperoned the writing of the book till the end and often owned it more than I did. Kanishka's enthusiasm for the book remained higher than mine. It was only after he approved the first draft that I had the confidence to send it to Pan Macmillan India.

Kanishka also introduced me to Sreeram Ramakrishnan, a young researcher and entrepreneur with a love for writing. Sreeram helped me with research and added important chunks of historical information when not coming up with new ideas to pitch to his clients.

The former publisher of Pan Macmillan India, Diya Kar Hazra, enthusiastically accepted the proposal that Kanishka pitched to her. I met and discussed the idea with Diya only after Kanishka had sealed the deal with Pan Macmillan. I am grateful to her for accepting an idea that many couldn't comprehend.

Sushmita Chatterjee, editor at Pan Macmillan India, took charge of the book seamlessly after Diya moved on. Sushmita and her team have been diligent editors, reducing fat and removing needless jargon.

Adrian Monck, Member of the Managing Board at WEF, was excited and encouraging about the book. His encouragement allowed me to press ahead with the idea with renewed enthusiasm.

The former president of Confederation of Indian Industry (CII), Naushad Forbes, and the current director general, Chandrajit Banerjee, offered unalloyed support for the project and were generous with advice and help. Chandrajit sent personal mails to several CEOs introducing the book idea and requesting them to share their experience and case studies with me. Marut Sengupta, Deputy Director General, CII, and Sharmila Kantha, Principal Consultant, CII, guided me in identifying the relevant sectors for research. Sharmila who has written about the journey of Indian industry in liberalized India had many interesting insights to share. She helped structure the book and its chapters.

I have to thank the CEOs and founders who agreed to share their experience and some business sensitive information about their projects that were initially at pilot stage. They believed that Indian companies must transform and invest in technology to stay ahead of global competition. These companies prefer to act and not just lament about the challenges they face. Among these CEOs, some took special interest and went out of their way to educate me on the subject. These include Harsh Mariwala, Chairman Marico Industries; Banmali Agrawala, former President and CEO, GE in India; Siraj Chaudhry, Chairman, Cargill India; Sanjiv Bajaj, MD, Bajaj Finserv; Rajeev Varman, CEO, Burger King India; Harsh Chitale, CEO, Philips Lighting India; Rajesh Magow, Co-founder, Make My Trip; Sanjeev Bhikchandani, Founder, Naukri.com; Anil Rai Gupta, Chairman, Havells India; and Shantanu Prakash, Founder, Educomp.

I met Pranav Pai, Founding Partner at 3one4 Capital, with his father, the irrepressible Mohandas Pai, at a meeting of the All India Management Association (AIMA). Pranav and I were speaking at a session on entrepreneurship. At the AIMA session, he spoke passionately about how start-ups must go beyond the popular app solutions to focus on real-life challenges in sectors like healthcare and agriculture. Pranav's fund invests in such companies with a clear focus on technologies like artificial intelligence. He readily agreed to introduce me to some start-ups featured in the book, who address ground realities in non-glamorous sectors.

I thank my parents, Saryu and SR Sharma, who make an effort to understand economic reforms and technology only because I write about them. And, of course, for inculcating a deep sense of learning and curiosity in me. Sanchita and our son, Aadi, have tolerated my many idiosyncrasies and erratic work hours. Sanchita was generous enough to lend her expertise on healthcare for the chapter.

My brother Prashant beat me to writing a book by a couple of years. He wrote an excellent and analytical work on the right to information act after his PhD at London School of Economics. He was thrilled that I was following his footsteps in writing. My late mother-in-law Renu Sharma was a source of constant encouragement to me. Her undiluted affection was always a source of energy for me. She almost single-handedly brought up our son and our Lhasa Apso, Dazzle. She would have cheered my effort with quiet pride.

And finally, I hope my son Aadi, who is studying computer science, will read this book and not remain unimpressed with my work. Millions of young twenty-year-olds like Aadi will grow up and join the workforce in the era of the Fourth Industrial Revolution. For them, artificial intelligence and robots will be everyday technology.

NOTES

Chapter 1: India and the Fourth Industrial Revolution

1. G Das, 'Going, Going, Gone: Automation Can Lead to Unprecedented Job Cuts in India', *Business Today*, 18 June 2017, http://www.businesstoday.in/magazine/cover-story/going-going-gone/story/253260.html
2. R Vlastelica, 'Bitcoin Makes Up Nearly Half of the $100 Billion Cryptocurrency Market Cap. What's the Rest?', *MarketWatch*, 23 June 2017, http://www.marketwatch.com/story/all-of-the-digital-money-in-the-world-in-one-chart-2017-06-07
3. R King, 'GE Adds More Predictive Capabilities, Partners to Industrial Internet Cloud', *ZDNet*, 9 October 2013, http://www.zdnet.com/article/ge-adds-more-predictive-capabilities-partners-to-industrial-internet-cloud/
4. See http://www.iiconsortium.org/about-us.htm
5. H Banthien, 'Implementation of an Industry 4.0 Strategy – The German Plattform Industrie 4.0', European Commission guest

blog, 25 January 2017, https://ec.europa.eu/digital-single-market/en/blog/implementation-industry-40-strategy-german-plattform-industrie-40

6. See http://www.plattform-i40.de/I40/Navigation/EN/ThePlatform/PlattformIndustrie40/plattform-industrie-40.htm
7. N Christopher, 'Growing Number of Private and PSBs Introducing Humanoid Robots to Answer Basic Customer Queries', *The Economic Times*, 30 June 2017, http://economictimes.indiatimes.com/industry/banking/finance/banking/growing-number-of-public-and-psbs-introducing-humanoid-robots-to-answer-basic-customer-queries/articleshow/59344522.cms
8. M Bhupta, 'India Faces 1.5 mn White-collar Job Crisis in Telecom, IT, BFSI', *MoneyControl*, 24 February 2017, http://www.moneycontrol.com/news/business/companies/india-faces-15-mn-white-collar-job-crisistelecom-it-bfsi-1034834.html
9. R Laha, 'Automation Impact: By 2021, One in Four Job Cuts May Be from India', *Livemint*, 3 March 2017, http://www.livemint.com/Industry/lElBJJHqEZBBKkQyL6ycyJ/Automation-impact-By-2021-one-in-four-job-cuts-may-be-from.html
10. PTI, '2 Lakh IT Engineers to Lose Jobs Annually in the Next 3 Years: Head Hunters India', *The Economic Times*, 14 May 2017, http://economictimes.indiatimes.com/tech/ites/it-to-layoff-up-to-2-lakh-engineers-annually-for-next-3-years-head-hunters-india/articleshow/58670563.cms
11. R Kurup, 'Unique Mobile Subscribers to Cross 5 Billion Globally This Year: GSMA', *BusinessLine*, 27 February 2017, http://www.thehindubusinessline.com/info-tech/unique-mobile-subscribers-to-cross-5-billion-globally-this-year-gsma/article9562225.ece
12. Promatics Technologies, 'Apps Economy Forecast – How App Store Revenue Will Go Through the Roof by 2021?', *WhaTech*, 7 July 2017, https://www.whatech.com/mobile-apps/news/332300-

apps-economy-forecast-how-app-store-revenue-will-go-through-the-roof-by-2021
13. S Pillai, 'India is World's Fourth-largest App Economy', *The Economic Times*, 7 July 2016, http://economictimes.indiatimes.com/tech/software/india-is-worlds-fourth-largest-app-economy-report/articleshow/53092793.cms
14. G Aulakh, 'Apple Is Making Phones in India, Tim Cook Tells Prime Minister Narendra Modi', *The Economic Times*, 27 June 2017, http://economictimes.indiatimes.com/tech/hardware/positive-on-india-made-se-iphones-app-developers-tim-cook-to-modi/articleshow/59320777.cms
15. M Murali and K Krishnamurthy, 'Five Cool Indian Startups Offering Drone Technology', *The Economic Times*, 18 April 2014, http://economictimes.indiatimes.com/slideshows/biz-entrepreneurship/five-cool-indian-startups-offering-drone-technology/drone-technology-startups/slideshow/33900000.cms
16. A Mahdawi, 'What Jobs Will Still Be Around in 20 Years?', *The Guardian*, 26 June 2017, https://www.theguardian.com/us-news/2017/jun/26/jobs-future-automation-robots-skills-creative-health
17. See Global Challenge Insight Report, 'The Future of Jobs', World Economic Forum, January 2016, www3.weforum.org/docs/WEF_Future_of_Jobs.pdf
18. S Kessler, 'One. That's How Many Careers Automation Has Eliminated in the Last 60 Years', World Economic Forum, 27 March 2017, https://www.weforum.org/agenda/2017/03/automation-has-totally-eliminated-just-one-career-in-the-last-60-years?utm_content=bufferc9144&utm_medium=social&utm_source=twitter.com&utm_campaign=buffer
19. R Hutt, 'Want a Job in 2025? These Are the Sectors to Focus on', World Economic Forum, 5 September 2016, https://www.

weforum.org/agenda/2016/09/job-in-2025-skills-sectors-to-focus-on

20. C Weller, 'From Robotics Vet to Holoportation Specialist, 5 Jobs That Could Exist by 2030', World Economic Forum, 2 September 2016, https://www.weforum.org/agenda/2016/09/from-robotics-vet-to-holoportation-specialist-5-jobs-that-could-exist-by-2030
21. E Amberber, 'In 2016, $4 Billion Invested in Indian Startups – Deal Value Decreased 55%, Volume Increased by 3% from 2015', *YourStory*, 31 December 2016, https://yourstory.com/2016/12/indian-startups-funding-report/
22. See http://www.wipro.com/holmes/
23. See report by KPMG and NASSCOM, 'Fintech in India', June 2016, https://assets.kpmg.com/content/dam/kpmg/pdf/2016/06/FinTech-new.pdf
24. V Sood, 'Rebooting Indian IT Industry', *Livemint*, 23 June 2017, http://www.livemint.com/Industry/B0VcHy8V2xZF6eXqWgv5BM/Rebooting-Indian-IT-industry.html
25. See http://www.nasscom.in/press/it-bpm-industry-sustained-growth-path-fy-2017-18-digital-solutions-and-niche-segments-key
26. R Venkatesan, 'Why This Is Indian IT Industry's Kodak Moment', *The Times of India*, 2 July 2017, http://timesofindia.indiatimes.com/home/sunday-times/all-that-matters/why-this-is-indian-it-industrys-kodak-moment/articleshow/59403402.cms
27. For more information, see http://indiastack.org/about/
28. See https://belong.co/talent-supply-index/

Chapter 2: Manufacturing

1. See report, 'Fridges and Washing Machines Liberated Women: Researcher', *Eurekalert*, 12 March 2009, https://www.eurekalert.org/pub_releases/2009-03/uom-aw031209.php

2. TNN and Agencies, 'Raymond to Replace 10,000 Jobs with Robots in Next 3 Years', *The Economic Times*, 16 September 2016, http://economictimes.indiatimes.com/jobs/raymond-to-replace-10000-jobs-with-robots-in-next-3-years/articleshow/54358700.cms
3. L D'Monte, 'Marico Taps Analytics for Growth', *Livemint*, 4 June 2015, http://www.livemint.com/Industry/PkjAud0lcXFc2H9egy0JQP/Marico-taps-analytics-for-growth.html
4. See CISCO white paper, 'The Zettabyte Era: Trends and Analysis', 7 June 2017, https://www.cisco.com/c/en/us/solutions/collateral/service-provider/visual-networking-index-vni/vni-hyperconnectivity-wp.html

Chapter 3: Logistics And Services

1. S Kohli, 'Transitioning Beyond Manually-run Warehouses', *Logistics Insight Asia*, 3 January 2016, https://www.logasiamag.com/2016/01/transitioning-beyond-manually-run-warehouses/
2. See excerpt from 'Virtual and Augmented Reality: Understanding the Race for the Next Computing Platform', *Goldman Sachs*, 13 January 2016, http://www.goldmansachs.com/our-thinking/pages/technology-driving-innovation-folder/virtual-and-augmented-reality/report.pdf
3. See press release, 'Successful Trial Integration of DHL Parcelcopter into Logistics Chain', DHL, 5 September 2016, http://www.dhl.com/en/press/releases/releases_2016/all/parcel_ecommerce/successful_trial_integration_dhl_parcelcopter_logistics_chain.html
4. P Ganguly and J Vignesh, 'Scientists building the next generation of technology for the logistics industry', *Economic Times*, 9 December 2016.
5. M Lierow, S Janssen and J D'Inca, 'Amazon Is Using Logistics to Lead a Retail Revolution', *Forbes*, 18 February 2016, https://

www.forbes.com/sites/oliverwyman/2016/02/18/amazon-is-using-logistics-to-lead-a-retail-revolution/3/#2f1995802a19
6. Z Schreiber, 'Amazon Logistics Service – The Future of Logistics?', SupplyChain247, 2 February 2016, http://www.supplychain247.com/article/amazon_logistics_services_the_future_of_logistics
7. F Tobe, 'While Amazon Doubles its Number of Warehouse Robots to 30K, Competing Systems Emerge', *Robohub*, 2 November 2015, http://robohub.org/while-amazon-doubles-its-number-of-warehouse-robots-to-30k-competing-systems-emerge/

Chapter 4: Consumer and Retail

1. A Ghose, 'The Value of Lighting Beyond Illumination for the Smart City', *Enterprise Innovation*, 8 May 2017, https://www.enterpriseinnovation.net/article/value-lighting-beyond-illumination-smart-city-1350591555

Chapter 5: Transportation and Mobility

1. A Raj, 'Robots Sweep Across Maruti Suzuki's Shop Floor', *Livemint*, 9 May 2017, http://www.livemint.com/Companies/0qexlea1C0MelXiAXcveOJ/Robots-sweep-across-Maruti-Suzukis-shop-floor.html
2. S Webzell, 'The Rise of Robotics', *Automotive Manufacturing Solutions*, 3 February 2015, http://www.automotivemanufacturingsolutions.com/technology/the-rise-of-robotics
3. M Dalal and A Sen, 'Uber India's Amit Jain: We want to take Travis Kalanick's vision forward', *Livemint*, 4 July 2017, http://www.livemint.com/Companies/KfdcZp0oBAQ5e1NFH2YBYJ/We-want-to-take-Traviss-vision-forward-Uber-Indias-Amit-J.html
4. S Chakraborty, 'Ola, Uber See Rides Rise Fourfold in 2016: Report', *Livemint*, 17 February 2017, http://www.livemint.com/

Companies/bjNzZDHCO25e0OZhj3okIJ/Ola-Uber-see-rides-rise-fourfold-in-2016-report.html

5. P Barter, 'Cars Are Parked 95% of the Time. Let's Check!', Reinventing Parking, 22 February 2013, http://www.reinventingparking.org/2013/02/cars-are-parked-95-of-time-lets-check.html
6. S Harwani, 'Passenger Vehicle Sales in India Double in a Decade', *Autocar Professional*, 2 September 2016, http://www.autocarpro.in/analysis-sales/passenger-vehicle-sales-india-double-decade-21595
7. PTI, 'India Eyes All-electric Car Fleet by 2030, Says Piyush Goyal', *Livemint*, 30 April 2017, http://www.livemint.com/Industry/JvyUPmrumUS832KL5 BKzhN/India-eyes-allelectric-car-fleet-by-2030-says-Piyush-Goyal.html
8. C Brodie, 'India Will Sell Only Electric Cars within the Next 13 Years', World Economic Forum, 23 May 2017, https://www.weforum.org/agenda/2017/05/india-electric-car-sales-only-2030/

Chapter 6: Healthcare and Diagnostics

1. I Lunden, 'Google Acquires India's Halli Labs, which Was Building AI Tools to Fix "Old Problems"', *TechCrunch*, 12 July 2017, https://techcrunch.com/2017/07/12/google-acquires-indias-halli-labs-which-was-building-ai-tools-to-fix-old-problems/
2. IANS, 'Google to Mentor 6 More Indian Start-ups in AI, Machine Learning', *YourStory*, 25 May 2017, https://yourstory.com/2017/05/google-to-mentor-6-more-indian-startups/
3. A Jayanthi, '10 Biggest Technological Advancements for Healthcare in the Last Decade', *Becker's Hospital Review*, 28 January 2014, http://www.beckershospitalreview.com/healthcare-information-technology/10-biggest-technological-advancements-for-healthcare-in-the-last-decade.html

4. See 'The Key Competitive Advantages of Medical Tourism Industry in India', Heidelberg Medical Consultancy, http://www.heidelbergmedical.com/blogs/173/the-key-competitive-advantages-of-medical-tourism-industry-in-india
5. Janakiram MSV, 'How Microsoft Is Making Big Impact With Machine Learning', *Forbes*, 30 July 2016, https://www.forbes.com/sites/janakirammsv/2016/07/30/how-microsoft-is-making-big-impact-with-machine-learning/#3c88cb472f16
6. See interview 'Robots and Automation in India: Healthcare, Medicine, More Set to Get a Shot in the Arm', *Electronics For You*, 10 March 2017, http://electronicsforu.com/market-verticals/automation/robots-automation-india-healthcare-medicine-set-get-shot-arm
7. See 'Home Health Care in India: In Search of the Right Business Model', *Knowledge @ Wharton*, 11 September 2014, http://knowledge.wharton.upenn.edu/article/home-health-care-india-search-right-business-model/
8. See diagram in http://www.lumibyte.eu/wp-content/uploads/2013/10/Bild4-uni-duesseldorf1.png

Chapter 7: Hospitality and Travel

1. See Sectoral Report, 'Tourism & Hospitality Industry in India', India Brand Equity Foundation, June 2017, https://www.ibef.org/industry/tourism-hospitality-india.aspx

Chapter 8: Banking and Finance

1. See report, 'Customer Experience Management Market Worth 13.18 Billion USD by 2021', *MarketsandMarkets*, http://www.marketsandmarkets.com/PressReleases/customer-experience-management.asp

2. See report by KPMG and NASSCOM, 'Fintech in India: A Global Growth Story', June 2016, https://assets.kpmg.com/content/dam/kpmg/pdf/2016/06/FinTech-new.pdf
3. See press release, 'ICICI Bank Introduces "Software Robotics" to Power Banking Operations', ICICIbank.com, 8 September 2016, https://www.icicibank.com/aboutus/article.page?identifier=news-icici-bank-introduces-software-robotics-to-power-banking-operations-20160809103646464
4. See report, 'Digital Disruption in the Insurance Sector', KPMG, 31 May 2017, https://home.kpmg.com/in/en/home/insights/2017/05/insurance-technology-robotics.html

Chapter 9: Agriculture And Food

1. TCA S Raghavan, 'India's Agricultural Yield Suffers from Low Productivity', *Livemint*, 9 September 2014, http://www.livemint.com/Opinion/nw9JKiPrDPpqCuWfmoibPN/Indias-agricultural-yield-suffers-from-low-productivity.html
2. IANS, 'Nearly 70 Per Cent of Indian Farms Are Very Small, Census Shows', *Business Standard*, 9 December 2015, http://www.business-standard.com/article/news-ians/nearly-70-percent-of-indian-farms-are-very-small-census-shows-115120901080_1.html
3. B Freese, 'Number of Farms in US Drops As Acreage Size Grows', *Agriculture*, 17 February 2017, http://www.agriculture.com/news/business/farms-in-us-drops-size-grows
4. See 'State of Indian Agriculture 2015-16', Ministry of Agriculture and Farmer's Welfare, Government of India, May 2016, http://eands.dacnet.nic.in/PDF/State_of_Indian_Agriculture,2015-16.pdf

Chapter 10: Education and Training

1. See report, 'Online Education in India: 2021', *KPMG*, 31 May 2017, https://home.kpmg.com/in/en/home/insights/2017/05/internet-online-education-india.html
2. See 'Report on Fifth Annual Employment – Unemployment Survey (2015-16)', vol. 1, Ministry of Labour and Employment, Government of India, http://labourbureaunew.gov.in/UserContent/EUS_5th_1.pdf
3. See press release, 'Gartner Says By 2020, a Quarter Billion Connected Vehicles Will Enable New In-Vehicle Services and Automated Driving Capabilities', Gartner, 26 January 2015, http://www.gartner.com/newsroom/id/2970017

INDEX